97

THROUGH
THE BARRIERS OF
DEAFNESS AND ISOLATION

Oral Communication of the Hearing-impaired Child
in Life Situations

THE MACMILLAN COMPANY
NEW YORK · CHICAGO
DALLAS · ATLANTA · SAN FRANCISCO
LONDON · MANILA
IN CANADA
BRETT-MACMILLAN LTD.
GALT, ONTARIO

THROUGH
THE BARRIERS OF
DEAFNESS AND
ISOLATION

Oral Communication of the
Hearing-impaired Child in Life Situations

BORIS V. MORKOVIN, Ph.D.
Emeritus Professor, University of Southern California

In collaboration with
LUCELIA M. MOORE, M.S.
University of Southern California

THE
MACMILLAN COMPANY
New York

First printing, September, 1960

Library of Congress catalog card number: 60–10773

The Macmillan Company, New York
Brett-Macmillan Ltd., Galt, Ontario

Printed in the United States of America

Dedicated to
parents and teachers who are helping
hearing-impaired children to become
a part of the hearing world

FOREWORD

As a learning theorist and student of human personality, I welcome the invitation of Dr. Morkovin and his collaborators to make some preliminary remarks concerning their interesting and extraordinarily useful little book, *Through the Barriers of Deafness and Isolation*.

Someone has said that the phenomenon of conditioning or associative learning "brings mind into being." And certainly an organism that can, on the basis of experience, come to react appropriately to sounds, sights, and smells, while still at a distance from the source thereof, has an enormous advantage over plants and the more primitive animals which lack this capacity.

But while necessary and important as a first step, the ability to form associations is, alone, not sufficient to create mind in the highest sense of the term. Here language is indispensable; and we well understand the concern of parents with its development in their children, their dismay when it is impeded, and their joy when it ultimately appears. One of the many fine features of this book is that it indicates so graphically what deafness in a child means both to the child himself and to his parents and would-be teachers and socializers.

Expensive experience has shown that speechreading is the most promising key for unlocking a child's mind from the prison of deafness and social deprivation. But, as the authors properly note, it is far more difficult to develop this skill and subsequent speech in children who have been deaf or seriously hard of hearing from birth or early infancy than it is to develop speechreading in individuals who already have normal speech before suffering a hearing impairment. Now, fortunately, we have a clear understanding of *why* this should be the case.

Normal infants are said to learn to talk "through imitation." This means, at a grossly descriptive level, that first they hear the speech of others, *in a meaningful context*, and then begin trying to reproduce it themselves. But what is equally important—and commonly over-looked—is that, in the process, they are also able to *hear themselves*. In this way they can correct, guide, and perfect their performance against the memory or images they have of the speech patterns of others. From others they get a mental standard of comparison; and, by means of the immediate auditory "feedback" from their own vocal be-havior, they can tell, quite precisely, when they are "tracking," i.e., matching the model, and when they are not.

However, in the child deaf from birth or early infancy, all this is changed. Since he cannot hear others, he has no auditory "model" for his own speech responses, regardless of whether he can to some degree hear himself or not. If the mouth movements which accompany speech in others are brought specifically to his attention, the child can, of course, *see* them; but he does not ordinarily see his *own* mouth move-ments. Thus, although he has ever so clear a memory or image of the mouth movements of others, he lacks the necessary visual feedback for comparing and guiding his would-be "imitative" reproduction thereof. Said otherwise, the deaf (but seeing) child, in this situation, ordinarily lacks a "knowledge of results" and so has an insurmount-able handicap in his learning efforts, unless given special assistance.

In several of the chapters of this book, allusion is made to the use of *mirrors* with children who are trying to speak by means of speech-reading. The practical importance of this technique cannot be over-emphasized: it provides the otherwise lacking *visual feedback* from the child's own mouth movements, so that he has an immediate check on "how he is doing." Now, with the aid of a mirror, the deaf child ap-proaches the advantageous position as regards speech learning that the normal hearing child has: like the latter, he has not only a *model* for speech behavior but also a means of gauging his success or fail-ure in approximating the model. Once an adult has grasped the *theory* behind so-called imitative or "reproductive" behavior in general, he will see why the use of mirrors is so important to the deaf child who is trying to learn to speak on the basis of visual stimulation from others *and from himself.*

However, it should be realized that visual feedback is by no means a perfect substitute for normal hearing. It is generally known among educators of the deaf that lip movements are often ambiguous and that not more than 40 per cent of them can be precisely identified. This is why it is important to supplement speechreading as extensively as possible with *other* sensory information, especially that to be derived from whatever residual hearing may be activated through the use of good hearing aids and from the tactile sensing of vibration. With coordinated, multisensory feedback to aid him, even a child with very grave hearing impairment can be greatly assisted in speech learning, especially if it is kept in mind that the word as produced by others must be sensed in as many ways as possible by the child and that he should then have the same sensory channels available to him when he himself tries to reproduce the word.

This brings us now, in a particularly compelling way, to an appreciation of the stress which Dr. Morkovin and his co-workers place upon the so-called "life-situation" method of teaching speech skills to deaf children. From the learning laboratory and, more particularly, from research with "talking birds,"[1] we know that before a living organism will try to recreate any given form of stimulation (originally provided by others), that stimulation must have acquired a "good" significance or meaning. If, on a succession of "trials," a tone is sounded and a hungry laboratory rat is given a morsel of food, the tone, as a result of its repeated association with food and hunger reduction, will become a *good* sound, one the rat wants to hear and will gladly reproduce if given a chance. And such a chance can be provided, for example, by means of a little metal bar, depression of which makes an electrical contact and "turns on" the tone. Now, although the act of pressing the bar produces no food (only tone), the rat will

[1] See "What Talking Birds Taught Me," *Reader's Digest,* March, 1958. Reprints of this article can be obtained from Mildred Hatch, 8 Pine Street, Saint Johnsbury, Vermont.

nevertheless press the bar several times (in a way it would not do if there were no tone), simply for the satisfaction which the *good sound* (tone) itself provides.

Something of a very similar kind is, of course, what normally happens to the words which mothers utter to hearing infants as they feed, bathe, and otherwise care for and "love" them. Mother's word sounds thus become *good* sounds, and soon the infant is vocally "fumbling around" (babbling) and trying to "find" and make them himself. At first the satisfaction that comes from approximating a mother sound is purely "autistic": the word noise accomplishes nothing "practical," only the pleasure associated with the sound as made by mother and "reinforced" by something good that followed. But eventually someone else hears these sounds as made by the baby and immediately there is a big reaction from the environment: "Hey," someone cries, "the baby just said . . . !" And for a few minutes, baby finds he is unexpectedly important—and papa and mama are assured that they have produced a real little human being!

Thus, to the satisfaction inherently associated with certain word sounds in the context of motherly loving is added the potent discovery that words are socially instrumental: they produce results of a highly *practical* nature. And so the stage is set for the continuous, ongoing series of developments which eventuates, by the age of five or six, in the mastery of that miracle of mind which we call human speech.

In principle, speech learning by the hearing-impaired child, *if* it occurs, follows much the same course, although there are important differences of detail. Here it is not mother sounds but mother *sights* (supported by residual hearing and by sensations of vibration derived through touch) which have to be associated with good things. Mrs. McArthur and Mrs. Stockman both give dramatic and moving accounts, in Part III, of how this can be done. But the efficiency of the procedure can, I believe, be considerably increased. Mrs. McArthur says that the movements of her mouth associated with the uttering of certain words "needed endless repetitions, perhaps a thousand," before these words, as "seen," came to mean for her little girl what they mean for the rest of us when heard, despite the fact that the repetition occurred in a real-life, meaningful, important situation. I would suggest that instead of the mother (or special teacher) merely exhibiting or pointing to some useful object and saying its name, the name-word, formed on the mother's lips, be a prelude or *cue* for the presentation of the object. Thus, for example, if a child likes grapes, the mother should have the grapes concealed, then, when the child is watching her mouth, say "grape," and produce a grape and give it to the child. Then a period of *waiting* (this is quite important), presently again (when the child is attentive) "grape," followed by a grape; and so on. With such a procedure, the deaf child will very quickly become interested in seeing the word "grape" formed on the mother's or teacher's lips; and, if the child is seated where he can *see himself*, he will, I predict, soon start trying to "hurry up" the appearance of the grape by producing the cue himself, i.e., making the same, "meaningful" movement sequence that he sees his mother make, as a prelude to his getting a grape.

I am confident that, if the parents and teachers of deaf children will master the *theory* of imitative learning as we understand it today, they can considerably improve the efficiency of their teaching methods. In fact, I conjecture (though without any actual evidence, as yet, to back it up) that the procedure involved in the "grape" example could be made still more efficient if child and mother or teacher were seated so they could see both themselves and each other *in the mirror*. This procedure should have the very considerable advantage of allowing the child to watch his mother's or teacher's mouth movements in a way that makes it very natural for him also to watch *his own*.

It should be constantly kept in mind that the most basic function of words (especially nouns) is that of obtaining, producing, calling for something, rather than just "talking about" it. First let a word response function *instrumentally;* its use for purely *representational* purposes will develop later, and quite naturally.

Finally, let me say a word about another outstanding feature of this book and what it stands for. Deaf children have sometimes been taught to speak through speechreading by very complicated and artificial procedures. By contrast, the techniques which the present authors advocate can be employed in situations that are natural and interesting for the child, thus involving him in the life of his family, neighborhood, playground, and community at the same time they are helping him to learn to speak. Such a program has, of course, much to recommend it; and I would only express the hope that to the beginnings of good practice, which this book abundantly illustrates, can be added a fuller explication and appreciation of underlying *theory*. Theory is the handmaiden of practicality, not its enemy!

O. Hobart Mowrer, Ph.D.
Research Professor
Department of Psychology
University of Illinois
Urbana, Illinois

June, 1960

ACKNOWLEDGMENTS

It is my privilege to give credit to the writers of this book who enthusiastically shared their firsthand experience and professional knowledge and skill in order to help the hearing-impaired child break "through the barriers of deafness and isolation." Special recognition should be given to Lucelia M. Moore. Her work with hearing-impaired children for many years has been the source and inspiration for the development of the "natural" or "functional" approach to speechreading in "life situations." Dr. Lowell C. Ruch, executive director of the Hearing Center of Metropolitan Los Angeles, assisted in compiling sources and information useful to teachers and parents of hearing-impaired children. Gratitude should be expressed to James H. Mason for his careful reading of the manuscript as well as to Margaret Starbuck for her help in preparing the book. The unsigned articles in this book were written by the author.

BORIS V. MORKOVIN, PH.D.

June, 1960

CONTENTS

Part IV. Oral Communication on the Concrete Conceptual Level

Section

Part V. Transition to Abstract Language

Part VI. The Hearing-impaired Child in "Integrated" Classes

Section

Part VII. Intensive Training in Speechreading with Life-Situation Films

Part VIII. On His Feet

Part IX. Conclusion

Part X. Appendixes

THROUGH
THE BARRIERS OF
DEAFNESS AND ISOLATION

Oral Communication of the Hearing-impaired Child
in Life Situations

PART I

INTRODUCTION

FUNCTIONAL APPROACH TO
ORAL COMMUNICATION

The authors of this book aim to create conditions for effective oral communication of hearing-impaired children.[1] The ability to communicate orally in the hearing and speaking world helps hearing-impaired children of normal intelligence to break through "the barriers of isolation," to adapt themselves to society, and to use their sensory and mental capacities. The senses and the brain, says Gardner Murphy in *Human Potentialities* (1958), serve as a "reality-mediating" system. For the full development and use of human potentialities, an effective early oral contact with the world is necessary.

New possibilities of oral contact with the world have been opened for a growing number of hearing-impaired children.[2] These children's sensory and mental capacities can now be utilized more fully, and the children can "integrate" more readily with the hearing and speaking world. In this book, authors from many fields have contributed to this integration by outlining a functional approach[3] to the development of children's oral communication. This approach is

[1] Hearing-impaired children include the *deaf* whose hearing is considered "nonfunctional" for ordinary conversation and the *hard of hearing* whose impaired hearing does not prevent their hearing ordinary conversation, with or without hearing aids. However, according to recent audiological research (see H. C. Huizing, 1959, p. 81), the boundaries between deaf and hard of hearing are not fixed, thanks to the availability of "potential hearing" in many deaf children. Dr. Huizing states that, by the use of sufficient amplification and by early auditory training, this "potential hearing" can be made more or less useful for learning to understand speech, for the acquisition of speech and language, or "only for the formation of a hearing controlled voice."

[2] H. C. Huizing, cf. *post*, p. 88.

[3] By using "life-situation" experience in training.

3

illustrated in many ways through the use of materials, procedures, and techniques which stimulate and facilitate oral communication.

Basically, the functional approach in helping a hearing-impaired child to learn to communicate orally makes rich use of all living and teaching situations which interest him and are of importance to him. The child practices oral communication while participating in activities and responding to many types of situations. In a variety of ways he satisfies his needs and is impelled to express himself in different group settings, whether the group is his family, the school, the playground, or the community.

Modern hearing aids are used profitably not only by the hard of hearing but by the moderately deaf[4] and in some cases by the profoundly deaf.[5] The appropriate fitting of wearable aids at an early age makes it possible to utilize effectively even small segments of hearing in the speech range.[6] While coordinating these remnants of hearing by special training with other sensory modalities, it is possible to broaden the child's channel of perception. The remnants of hearing in the speech range are perceived by the child in speechreading simultaneously with the movements of the lips of the speaker. The perception of audiovisual cues of speech is reinforced by the association of these cues with the child's awareness of the kinesthetic and rhythmic movements of his speech organs and by the tactile sensation of the sound vibrations on his or another's cheeks and throat. This multisensory perception of speech is vitalized by actional situations to which speech is attached and which he understands well from situational context.

The child's first oral group is his family. He participates as a member in simple everyday situations and becomes integrated into an oral environment. Spurred on by a growing feeling of belonging to the family circle, he learns to orient himself to its routine and play activities. He learns to imitate the speech of persons whom he loves and accepts as models.

[4] Moderately deaf: 60 to 80 decibels (db) loss in speech range.
[5] Profoundly deaf: 80 or more db loss in speech range.
[6] Speech range: 500, 1000, 2000 cycles per second (cps).

Later he enters the larger world of school, and new social forces enter into the dynamics of his give-and-take relationships. The great variety of activities in which he participates contributes to his ability to express himself successfully in an oral atmosphere. He receives a new incentive to live up to the expectations of his new groups and to abide by the rules of the social game. He is motivated to cope with new and ever more complex situations. Teaching situations are enriched by an extensive use of visual aids, excursions, exhibits, and experiments. Reading and writing are new means of communication. He begins to build a reservoir of language, and as he learns to use words they become instruments for effective social interplay, interwoven into the pattern of his thinking and behavior. He sees the power of language as he is influenced by it and as he uses it to influence others. His ability to use language coincides with his ability to adapt himself to his new environment.

Many new avenues are opening up to facilitate the entrance of the hearing-impaired child into the normal hearing environment. This book was prepared with the child's integration into a normal world of spoken communication as its primary goal. The materials and practices presented here were intended as extracurricular material for the development of oral communication and not as a substitute for the school curriculums. The procedures are used to enrich the child's active language and to vitalize his oral communication; at the same time, they instill language principles by constant practice. A successful oral communication paves the way for formal study of language and academic subjects. The ability of the child to converse and receive verbal instruction grows. He dramatizes the subjects he studies and connects them with his expanding interests. He develops the intellectual and social skills needed for successful oral communication. He gains initiative as he explores the world, builds social relationships, and applies his knowledge in self-expressive ways.

The training of a hearing-impaired child to take an active part in the hearing world is a serious challenge. It cannot be fully met without the cooperative efforts of understanding and resourceful parents, teachers, audiologists, psychologists, and others, working together as a team. All members of the team should have a clear understanding of the extent of the barriers of deafness, and of the social isolation which results from the impoverishment of experiences and the blocking of learning. They must find ways of releasing the maximal and optimal forces within the child as he learns to relate to his environment. Educational devices and materials must be selected and planned in relation to the child's personality and the measure of his communicative powers and his social and intellectual growth.

This book was prepared by a number of writers, each contributing from his special field—a psychologist, an otologist, an audiologist, parents, therapists, and teachers, the latter group representing different schools which vary in their policies and practices. However, all the members of the group are unified in the belief in the importance of oral communication, in the need for early utilization of every training opportunity, and in developing the maximum of the child's sensory and mental potentialities.

It is believed that the cooperative research is timely and appropriate for the investigation of the impact of different environments, educational procedures, and methods of treatment upon the development of children with impaired hearing. In fact, it is not too much to hope that, as Dr. Huizing has predicted, this type of cooperative research will eventually modify the psychopedagogical standards of the hearing-impaired children.[7]

Bibliography

Davis, Hallowell (ed.). *Hearing and Deafness.* Rinehart & Company, Inc., New York, 1947.

Huizing, H. C. "Deaf-Mutism—Modern Trends in Treatment and Prevention," *Advances in Oto-Rhino-Laryngology,* 5:74–106, 1959. (S. Karger, Basel/New York.)

Morkovin, Boris V. "Rehabilitation of the Aurally Handicapped through the Study of Speechreading in Life Situations," *Journal of Speech*

[7] H. C. Huizing, cf. *post,* p. 91.

Disorders, **12**:363–68, 1947.

Morkovin, Boris V., Joseph M. Kinkade, and Donald R. Caziarc. *Aural Re-education, Psychological and Therapeutic Aspects.* University of Southern California Bookstore, Los Angeles, 1946, 43 pp.

Mowrer, O. H. *Psychotherapy: Theory and Research.* The Ronald Press Company, New York, 1958.

Murphy, Gardner. *Personality, a Biosocial Approach to Origins and Structure.* Harper & Brothers, New York, 1947.

Murphy, Gardner. *Human Potentialities.* Basic Books, Inc., New York, 1958.

PART II

MEDICAL, AUDIOLOGICAL, AND PSYCHOLOGICAL CONSIDERATIONS

SECTION 1

THE ROLE OF THE FAMILY
IN THE HABILITATION OF
A HEARING-IMPAIRED CHILD

The early initiative and cooperation of the family are necessary for a successful habilitation of their hearing-impaired child. When the family suspects that their child has a hearing loss, they should immediately consult both an otologist and an audiologist, and then cooperate with them. Having learned the truth that their child does not hear, the parents may find the experience an upsetting one. They may have to summon all their courage to face the facts and remain calm. At the same time, they should not be passive and feel sorry for themselves. They should do their utmost to make their child feel that he is accepted as he is, wanted and loved, regardless of his handicap.

This positive attitude of the parents is one of the most important factors in starting the child on the right road to speaking and to adapting himself to the hearing world. If they can make the child feel that he is a part of the family, he will soon learn to assert himself in little everyday situations and to imitate the speech of the members of his family.

The family should be instructed and guided by an audiologist and a teacher of the preschool deaf child.[1] Exercises can be given to utilize his residual hearing and to make use of his sensory and mental capacities. By involving the child in an active life of interest and

[1] Very helpful is a correspondence course like that offered by the John Tracy Clinic (see Bibliography, Part II, p. 28) where instructions are given to parents and teachers.

11

fascination, the parents prevent his social isolation and experiential deprivation and thus liberate his native intelligence from the imprisonment of deafness.

The family should continue to play their important role in helping their child to adjust himself to school and to new social groups. While assisting the child in solving his new problems, they should help him to become progressively more self-reliant, to learn to stand on his own feet.

At the same time, parents of the deaf must be realistic about finding out the limitations of their deaf children. Many deaf children, especially if they cannot use a hearing aid effectively, have great difficulty in acquiring fluent oral communication.

SECTION 2

MEDICAL ASPECTS OF THE HEARING-IMPAIRED
by
Norton Canfield, M.D.[1]

The ultimate goal of medical care is to prevent the development of abnormalities which impair the function of any part of the human body.

The everyday life of the normal sociable individual is so dependent upon hearing that it is difficult for those with good hearing to appreciate the confusion and frustration which accompany an appreciable hearing impairment. Hearing ranks with vision as being the most valuable human asset except for the mind itself. Within the realm of medicine much remains to be done to prevent hearing loss. As research delves deeper into the mysteries of the ear, prevention of

[1] Associate Clinical Professor of Otolaryngology, Yale University School of Medicine, New Haven, Connecticut.

hearing loss and successful medical and surgical treatment of those already impaired are gradually being attained.

Hereditary Factors in Human Hearing

At the time of conception, our genetic heredity is settled. Some human characteristics are so definite that they can be predicted according to the established laws of heredity. Hearing heredity, however, is very complex. The human generation is so long that geneticists cannot make controlled experiments with human beings to test their theories. There is at present no clear-cut picture of exactly what genes are involved in the inheritance of deafness. There is pedigree evidence that certain forms of perceptive impairment are hereditary and that two complementary genes are involved. It is this duplex heredity which can produce all normal progeny, although both parents may be deaf.

Today the otologist recognizes that heredity plays an important role in some kinds of hearing impairment. He cannot determine, however, with certainty if or how it will be expressed in the children of a particular couple. The deaf tend to intermarry because of their association in schools and special groups. This increases the number of the hereditarily deaf in the general population. Alexander Graham Bell noted a trend more than seventy years ago. He studied the population of Martha's Vineyard and noted that it was becoming, through inbreeding and assortative mating, a deaf group of the human race.

It may be that some individuals lose their hearing because of a hereditary weakness which makes them susceptible to deafness-producing conditions such as scarlet fever, German measles, ear infections, or even loud noises. When the question of inheritance of impaired hearing is posed to the otologist, he should first make a diagnosis of the condition. If it is of a type which is thought to be hereditary, the case should be referred to one of the seven medical genetic centers in the United States, a list of which can be obtained from the American Genetics Association at 1507 M Street N.W., Washington 5, D.C.

Congenital Hearing Loss

Subsequent to the influence of the hereditary genes, but prior to birth, intrauterine environment can affect the hearing mechanism. Maternal infections, notably the virus diseases, especially the virus disease of rubella (German measles), sometimes affect the development of the unborn child. During the first three months of fetal life, the ear is particularly susceptible to the damaging effect of virus infections. This was not fully appreciated until about 1946.

Consequently in many children born deaf, the defect was thought to be the result of a hereditary factor, when, in fact, the deficiency was the result of a virus infection. Since every child, however, whose mother had rubella during the first three months of his intrauterine life does not have hearing defects, an unidentified heredity trait may protect some children and not others. Probably only about 20 per cent of the children whose mothers had rubella during the first three months of gestation are so affected.

When the virus diseases can be controlled by proper vaccines, a potent preventive measure will be available. Another segment of our population will then be protected. Even today, exposure of women to rubella before their first pregnancy is advocated. This has obvious practical difficulties but it is not impossible. The medical profession knows what can be done, but our social progress sometimes lags. This is such an important matter, however, that prenatal advice immediately after conception can warn of certain possibilities, and if the pregnant mother is exposed to another person with rubella, protective gamma globulin may prevent an attack of rubella. The disease is often so light and of so little inconvenience to the mother that it may be regarded as of no significance or even pass unnoticed.

Other virus diseases in the pregnant mother may cause defective hearing in the unborn child. Influenza and the adenoviruses have been considered as possible offenders, but the evidence has not been completely verified. Even high fevers of unknown origin may damage the developing fetal organ of hearing.

If the mother has taken large doses of quinine during pregnancy, the developing ear may suffer a defect. In regions where malaria is prevalent, quinine was formerly an important drug to control the fever. Newer preparations now used to control malaria do not seem to have this same detrimental effect on the ears. Thus, this cause of congenital hearing loss is diminishing.

Developmental anomalies, the causes of which are not known, can cause hearing abnormalities even before birth. Malformations involving the middle ear and the external canal are associated with conductive loss, due to the obstruction of sound waves on their route to the inner ear. These deformities take the form of atresias or absence of the external canal, often associated with the deformity of the pinna which is called microtia.

A mysterious condition associated with incompatibility of the blood of the newborn child with the mother's blood serum causes a group of diseases known as erythroblastosis fetalis.[2] Severe deafness is one of the peculiar defects which have been definitely traced to these diseases. Unless prenatal tests are performed and appropriate measures instituted, the hearing of the newborn child may be severely impaired. Prevention of the sequelae of this type of blood dyscrasia is often possible, and examination of the blood of pregnant mothers should be performed before the child is born. This cause of early hearing loss is not a major one from the standpoint of numbers of children. But when it does cause hearing loss, the catastrophe for that child can be a major one. The exact location of the lesion is still controversial. Some investigators have placed it in the cochlea, some in the central nervous system, but both the cochlea and central nervous system nuclei have been the site of demonstrable lesions. Athetoid deformities, sometimes associated with aphasia, may be confused with or exist in addition to actual defects of the hearing mechanism.

Prematurity, twin births, placenta previa, and newborn children who require incubation and oxygen after birth are associated with hearing defects. The auditory nuclei are particularly sensitive to

---

[2] *Erythroblastosis fetalis* results from a blood-group incompatibility—one of them being the Rh factor (positive or negative).

hypoxia[3] and probably partially degenerate if the supply of oxygen is insufficient. Traumatic labor when the life of the child or mother or both are endangered may be responsible for hypoxia in paranatal life. In addition to hearing defects, the child may have cerebral palsy, which further complicates the clinical picture and causes difficulty in determining the extent of any possible hearing loss.

Ear Infections in Early Life

Since the introduction of the first chemotherapeutic agent, prontosil, in 1935, the toll of hearing loss from ear infections has declined steadily. Otologists were prompt in the use of this drug and those which have followed in rapid succession. Fortunately the blood supply to the ear when infection ensues can carry sufficient quantity of an antibacterial drug to effect rapid cure in something over 90 per cent of the cases.

Penicillin, first used in 1942, soon became the choice antibiotic drug for ear infections. Although many other antibiotics have been developed since and must sometimes be used, penicillin is still the best for most of the infections of the ear. Synthetic penicillin has recently been released to the medical profession. Hence, another important development will help prevent ear infections, some of which even now are not adequately treated by antibiotics.

All has not been well with some of the antibiotics used to treat ear and other infections within the human body. Some of the preparations, while effective in the control of the bacterial invasion, have been detrimental to hearing. Some antibiotics used to control specific infections such as tuberculosis, for which penicillin is ineffective, have affected the ear in several respects. Streptomycin, in the early days of its use, affected the balancing mechanism of the ear and occasionally the hearing apparatus in addition. Dihydrostreptomycin, used later, has had a most detrimental effect on many ears. In these cases, hearing has been so adversely affected that this drug should never be used in any form systemically unless it is the only drug which can save a life, or unless it is used in a patient whose hearing in both ears is already profoundly affected.

[3] *Hypoxia*—deficiency in oxygen.

Not only dihydrostreptomycin but neomycin and kanamycin have the same detrimental effect on the hearing of some patients. These also should never be used except as noted above. New antibiotics are constantly being developed. They can be tested on animals before ever being used on humans to determine any possibility of hearing loss. So important is this phase of our rapidly progressive drug industry that all doctors should be fully assured that any new medicine has been carefully tested for any possible ototoxic effect before prescribing it.

Although the antibiotics have been a tremendous boon for those who develop ear infections, another condition causing hearing loss has increased in frequency. As the middle-ear infections subside during the use of "wonder drugs," there often remains within the cavity of the middle ear a secretion which impairs the proper functioning of the conductive mechanism. When a patient appears cured, pain disappears and the eardrum may even return to a normal appearance, but the hearing does not return to its preinfection level. Hence the need for complete audiometry after every ear infection. If the hearing loss has not returned to normal, the otologist will consider the possibility of further treatment. Certain medicines such as the antihistamines and the anti-inflammatory drugs may affect a reduction in the inner-ear secretions. If these methods fail, the mechanical removal of the abnormal contents of the middle ear is mandatory. This can usually be done by aspiration through the eardrum, repeatedly if necessary. If the secretions are not removed, adhesions in the middle ear may occur, thereby preventing proper movement of the drum and the ossicular chain with consequent permanent hearing impairment. Treatment at this late stage is less effective and often completely unsuccessful.

Hearing Loss in Later Life

While prevention of impaired hearing is the ultimate goal, there is an increasing number of people in each decade of life whose hearing is permanently affected. These require the careful analytical evaluation of the otologist. He will then decide on a course of action to restore hearing if possible, to alleviate any annoying tinnitus which may accompany it, and set the patient on a course of auditory rehabilitation if hearing improvement by medical or surgical treatment is not successful.

Hearing Evaluation

For any working concept of a person's sense of hearing, a sense so psychologically involved in his life, specific information of the effect of the impairment on that person's life is essential. A careful history of onset, how the hearing loss has been accepted, wherein it is important to that patient, and something of the economic impact should be reviewed. Desires and ambitions are so variable in different people that advice or treatment for one person may be entirely wrong for another. Before examination and testing, a preliminary review to determine the type of patient will guide the otologist's steps toward his final advice. A few minutes of questions will usually reveal the real problems involved when a patient gives as his chief complaint that he "can't hear."

Following the interview, the otologist will make his physical examination to determine if any obstruction can cause the loss. Sometimes impacted cerumen, foreign bodies, or the products of infection block the external auditory canals. Nasopharyngeal swellings due to infection and allergy may obstruct the eustachian tube, through which air passes from the nose to the ear to maintain normal pressure on both sides of the drum membrane.

The functional examination of the hearing itself is next performed. Thanks to the tremendous advances in electronic devices, our audiometric apparatus is highly refined. The control of sound has reached a point of accuracy beyond most demands of clinical application. But, because of the complexity of our present testing instruments, there has developed a need for professional skill far greater than a few years ago. Research is constantly evolving new concepts of hearing analysis which will increase our ability to understand and apply therapeutic measures to more of our deafened patients.

With the history, physical examination, and functional testings specifically available for one whose hearing is impaired, the otologist then has a solid mass of information to proceed with advice to that patient. For a few, possibly 10 per cent of those who seek advice, an actual hearing improvement can be effected. For children the percentage is much higher. As the decades pile up, the percentage decreases. The population over sixty-five contains very few whose essential hearing is changed by any treatment other than the removal of obstructions from the auditory canal, eustachian tubes, or by the healing processes of an acute infection. Age takes its toll of the hearing of many in spite of any preventive measures now known. Once the neural elements of the hearing mechanism are permanently changed, a reversal of the pathologic process whereby function is restored cannot be expected.

Operations to Improve Hearing

When the neural elements of hearing are intact and impairment is present, a mechanical obstruction to the passage of sound to the cochlea causes the loss. Obvious obstructions in the external auditory canal can be removed surgically. When the obstruction is within the middle ear, it can, in many cases, be circumvented or decreased.

The fenestration operation, whereby sound enters the cochlea by a surgically produced route, has restored hearing in many thousands. The amount of human hearing that has been regained thereby would be impossible to measure. It can be said, however, that this milestone in clinical practice has not only brought new life and better living to many but the methods used have resulted in an upsurge of interest and courage to develop new and better techniques.

The stapes mobilization operation, whereby the chain of middle-ear ossicles is rearranged to increase their conductive efficiency, has had a rebirth. First done in the latter part of the nineteenth century but abandoned because of unfortunate complications, operating on the ossicles is now possible without the untoward side effects encountered earlier. The antibiotics and refinements of surgical techniques made possible with the lighted dissecting microscope now offer a method whereby residual hearing is greatly improved in cases of conductive loss due to otosclerosis. Not only does this disease yield to a mechanical approach, but the observations and discoveries made during this procedure are leading the otologist to a better understanding of auditory function. New procedures are evolving and previously unknown facts concerning the ear are becoming common knowledge among the progressive professionals in the field.

The medical profession is not satisfied with present methods. Complications do occur, and patients who are contemplating surgery must be fully prepared for disappointments. The psychological aspects of surgical failure require mature consideration on the part of the professional advisers if we are to avoid undue misery from an ill-conceived approach to the deafened individual.

If Medical or Surgical Therapy Is Ineffective

The great strides in restoring hearing-impaired individuals to a satisfactory communication status following World War I, and even more effective methods developed during and after World War II have opened new vistas of hope and achievement comparable with other professional fields of accomplishment. When the hearing level cannot be sufficiently restored, the auditory function which is available can then be used to greater advantage.

Hearing aids have been developed to a high degree of satisfaction. Great credit is due the scientific progress of the electronic engineer working in an atmosphere of enlightened industrial practice. But the hearing aids available do not solve problems for all. The altered sound which the impaired ear receives through an aid often evokes a neurologic response which is so foreign to the interpretation centers in the brain that perception of the correct sound message is not possible. Far more knowledge of the functioning processes of the impaired ear compared to the normal is needed before hearing aids can be a satisfactory solution for many people with hearing defects.

In addition to hearing aids, training programs are designed to readjust the whole person to his handicap. Auditory training and speechreading often add an increased communication ability that will lift many a person from just below to well above a level of satisfactory auditory perception. The person's motivation, his needs for good hearing, and the professional advice and training he receives will determine the final level on which his hearing serves his desires and ambitions.

Medical contributions to the hearing handicap are helpful when accurate evaluation of the auditory status is made and when all possible means to restore lost function are completed. In addition, the individual must be properly advised and encouraged to accept hearing aids, followed by nonmedical professional programs designed to re-educate him in undertaking and using the residual hearing ability to the best possible advantage.

SECTION 3

THE USE OF HEARING AIDS AND THE DEVELOPMENT OF SOUND AWARENESS
by
E. W. Johnson[1]

Extending the Use of Hearing Aids

The utilization of transistors in hearing aids in the last few years has practically revolutionized the hearing aid industry. It has permitted more powerful instrumentation in smaller and smaller packages. Other developments in hearing aids have greatly extended the

---

[1] E. W. Johnson, Ph.D., clinical audiologist, Otologic-Medical Group, Los Angeles. His daughter, Linda, a profoundly deaf child (250 cps/80 db, 500 cps/100 db), is wearing a binaural hearing aid, and attends an integrated school (Lawndale, California).

use to the majority of all hearing-impaired children, regardless of the severity of the loss. A few years ago it was considered useless to place a hearing aid on a child with only fragmentary responses or tiny islands of hearing. Today, the child who responds to only one or two frequencies on the audiometer can benefit from properly selected aids. For example, the profoundly deaf child whose only response is 250 or 500 cps at maximum loss levels can learn to respond to many environmental sounds, such as an automobile horn, a slamming door, and even to his own name. The parents of such a child are much more at ease when he is riding his bicycle down the street, knowing that he will respond to auto traffic. The child is made aware of many of the everyday background noises and as a result feels more a part of his normal environment. Moreover, it has been established that such a person is a better speechreader with a hearing aid on than without. Interestingly enough, even with very limited residual hearing, the use of two aids (and hence two ears) is often much more satisfactory than one aid alone.

The guiding principles in the use of hearing aids with young deaf children may be simply stated as follows:

1. Recent improvements in hearing aids have made practical, powerful aids in small units, making true binaural hearing feasible for most children.

2. The amount of benefit derived from hearing aids will vary from one child to another, depending greatly upon the amount of residual hearing. However, there are distinct benefits even for the profoundly deaf child with little, if any, response on the audiometer.

3. Hearing aids should be placed on the child as soon as a reasonably accurate appraisal of the amount of loss has been determined.

Developing Sound Awareness in the Profoundly Deaf Child

Parents of a young profoundly deaf child are often so overwhelmed with the immensity of the problem that they overlook the everyday opportunities of helping the child. In some instances the parents cannot accept the reality of deafness in the child. When the diagnosis of profound deafness has been made, they react by beginning a round of doctor visitations in the hope that one of the doctors will contradict the initial diagnosis. Other parents are too stunned to do much other than wait to see if the child outgrows the problem, or wait for professional help to relieve them of their frustrations. On the other hand, parents may face the reality of the child's deafness by putting on hearing aids as early as possible, by calling the child's attention to lip movements, and by developing an awareness of environmental sounds.

This section is concerned with ways in which parents of profoundly deaf children may help the youngsters become aware of different sounds and begin discrimination and differentiation of sound stimuli. The beginning of a sound-awareness program need not wait for the otologist's diagnosis, for manifold opportunities exist even in infancy. Although it is true that in some cases otological examination will establish severe deafness in an infant only a few months or even a few weeks old, in most cases such a diagnosis is not made much before the first birthday. Yet the observant parent, especially if this is not the first child, may become aware of the infant's lack of response to sound stimuli from the first few weeks to the first few months in the home. The mother may have noted that the child reacts to light stimuli—to switching on the ceiling light or to raising the shades—but that he does not respond to calling his name softly or even to clapping hands above his head. Even at this early age, holding the child close and calling his name or talking and singing into his ear, she may give him some concept of sound although, of course, speech will have no specific meaning.

After a hearing aid has been fitted (and preferably two aids with two separate amplifiers, microphones, volume controls, and with an ear mold for each ear), it will be much easier to get his attention for many environmental sounds. Such gross noises as clapping the hands above his head, banging toys against the crib, and slamming the door will be picked up and perceived by the child. As he matures we can expect that he will begin to associate certain sounds with certain acts. Thus, the slamming of the nursery door means that someone is coming to see him, to pay him attention, to talk to him. Very early the child may learn to associate the excited barking of a dog with the arrival of guests to the house. The honking of the car horn and the slam of the car door may mean that Daddy is coming home. At breakfast, the clank of the spoon against the cereal bowl, the ping of the milk bottle against the glass as milk is poured, even the sizzle of the frying bacon may be picked up if the loss is not too severe and if good hearing aids are provided. The sound of the vacuum cleaner and the ringing of the doorbell or the telephone may be picked up by some children and completely obscured from others. These are realistic life situations whereby the child may attach meaning to everyday home situations and to the noises and sounds of the home.

Remember that all children—normal and deaf children—will babble at certain age levels. This babbling process may start at five or six months and continue to approximately eighteen months. Normal hearing children, pleased with the babbling sounds they create, will continue to produce and perfect speech sounds. The deaf child, since he is unable to hear his voice, will at a certain point stop the babbling process. Babbling should be encouraged, and with properly fitted hearing aids some of this may be monitored and therefore repeated by the child.

With increasing maturation of the child, the beginning of specific word discrimination may be attempted. This may best be approached through the use of real objects such as a banana, an orange, a toy airplane, a red rubber ball. You may say, "Johnnie, this is a banana. This is a ball, a red ball. This is an orange. This is an airplane." By drilling on one or two objects, saying the name of the object over and over and letting Johnnie feel and handle the object, you may teach him to associate the movement of the lips, the sound that he hears, and the form of the object. Again, with good hearing aids and with a loss that is not too fragmentary, he may be able to differentiate by sound alone the different objects as you work with him. Specific word training, however, lies more in the province of the professional speech therapist and audiologist, who has been trained to work with the deaf and hard-of-hearing child. But there are countless opportunities for the parent to call certain activities, objects, and events to the attention of the child and to associate some sounds with that particular event.

In short, from early in the morning until bedtime, the normal hearing child is bombarded with a constant stream of environmental sound. The deaf child with his hearing aids may also be bombarded with sound, but this sound will have little meaning unless and until we can call attention to specific events and associate these events with the immediate sound that is heard. Parents will not replace trained teachers and therapists, but can give important early sound-awareness training for the deaf and severely hard-of-hearing child.

It is desirable to utilize all of the possible channels of sensory perception not only for purposes of better communication, but also to enrich the experiences of the child. While wearing his hearing aid, he can be introduced to music through a phonograph, radio, or television set. It is helpful to place his fingers against the diaphragm of the loud-speaker so that he can get the tactile sensation as well as the effect of the sound of the music through his hearing aid. Likewise, if the fingers are placed against the sounding board of the piano while the piano is being played, he will begin to associate the rhythm patterns of music with certain sensations conveyed to the tactile and hearing sense organs.

SECTION 4

THE MOTHER'S ATTITUDE TOWARD HER CHILD'S HANDICAP

The case of Billy S., who was treated by Mrs. Alathena J. Smith, may be more complicated than an average case of a deaf child, for in addition to his severe hearing handicap he has poor vision. However, this case indicates that the mother's negative and confused attitude may affect the very core of the mother-child interpersonal relationship, and can lead to serious emotional deprivation on the part of the child.

The mother is the connecting link between the child and the outside world. If a warm relationship and understanding do not exist between the mother and the child, he may become isolated and retarded in his growth and development. On the other hand, a close bond of affection and contact open the road for a give-and-take between the mother and the child. This affectionate contact with the mother gives rise to further stimulating interaction of the child with the rest of the family and his environment.

SECTION 5

COURAGE TO KNOW THE TRUTH
by
Alathena J. Smith[1]

The attitude of a hearing-impaired child toward himself reflects the feeling of his family about him and his handicap. If his parents, even without realizing it themselves, do not accept their child's handicap, he cannot help but be deeply influenced by their attitude. His whole physical, mental, and emotional development are affected by this attitude. His ability to project himself into his social environment and to explore it is hampered by the unfavorable attitude.

In his Foreword to this book Dr. O. Hobart Mowrer stresses the fact that it is important for the child to identify himself with his parents. As a counselor of parents, I find constant confirmation of this importance. Recently, I was alerted over the attitude of a mother of a hearing-impaired child whose hearing the audiologist tested in our clinic.[2] The audiologist noticed the strange way in which the mother

[1] Ph.D., Diplomate in Clinical Psychology, The John Tracy Clinic, Los Angeles.

[2] Billy S. is three years old and has a loss of hearing in 250 cps/85 db and in 500 cps/80 db. No residual hearing was discovered in other frequencies.

held her child. When consulting the mother, I was not surprised to see that instead of holding the child she put him on the floor, where he soon fell asleep. Later on, when she picked him up from the floor she handled him like an inanimate object. The mother soon admitted she had difficulty in relating herself to the child. Yet she displayed a concern about him. She spent many a sleepless night worrying about "what she could do to reach the child." She felt deeply inadequate in her personal relationship to him: "I do not think I am different from any normal mother but I am working in the dark. I know it is not enough to take care of only the physical needs of the child. I want to find the way to his response. I feel so unhappy because he does not pay attention to any of my words. He heeds only my emphatic, 'No, no!' when I try to stop him from doing something he shouldn't. I do not know how to make him want to do the right things, how to penetrate to him, how to begin to work positively instead of negatively. Obviously he is frustrated and angry because he doesn't know what is going on around him. Yet he has made remarkable progress in his muscular coordination and handling of objects and, in spite of his partial loss of sight, he recognizes objects."

As our therapeutic session progressed, the mother's tension subsided and she confided in me her doubts and remorses. It was hard enough for her to accept the sight impairment of the child but she did it because she knew what it was from having poor vision herself. She continued, "I suspected for some time that my son was deaf also. Others maintained that it was only my imagination and that he was not paying attention. But the lack of his response sometimes made me desperate. I felt so utterly helpless."

In the course of the counseling and after the mother was given the results of her child's hearing test, she finally said, "Now, today, after talking with you and after you have told me that my son is deaf, I am feeling a strange relief. I have the answer to all my doubts, whether I am doing some wrong things, and what I can do to help him besides taking care of his physical needs only. I feel firmer ground under my feet. Now I know why he is not responsive. After talking with you I know there are many ways of reaching his responses. I know that I can find ways to communicate with him and I will be helped in finding them. There are people who will guide me. Even before my son is able to enter a nursery school or kindergarten, I will be able to do a lot for him. I know he can be taught. I don't feel as helpless as I did before I came here."

Bibliography

Bergman, Moe. "Binaural Hearing," *A.M.A. Archives of Otolaryngology,* 66:572–78, (Nov.) 1957.

Bordley, John E. "The Problem of the Pre-School Child (Diagnostic Methods and the Otologist's Role in His Rehabilitation)," *Laryngoscope,* 62:514–20, (May) 1952.

Canfield, Norton. *Hearing, a Handbook for Laymen,* Doubleday & Company, Inc., New York, 1959.

Goda, Sidney, and Ray Smith. "Speech Stimulation Practices among Mothers of Pre-School Children," *Journal of Speech and Hearing Disorders,* 24:150–53, (May) 1959.

House, Howard P. "The Modern Management of Impaired Hearing," *Chicago Medical Society Bulletin,* 55:225–28, (Sept. 27) 1952.

John Tracy Clinic Correspondence Course for Parents of Little Deaf Children, 2–5 years of age. 806 W. Adams Blvd., Los Angeles 18, California.

Myklebust, Helmer R. *Your Deaf Child, a Guide for Parents.* Charles C Thomas, Publisher, Springfield, Ill., 1950.

Naunton, Ralph F. "The Effect of Hearing Aid Use upon the User's Residual Hearing," *Laryngoscope,* 67:569–76, (June) 1957.

Newby, Hayes A. *Audiology, Principles and Practice,* Chap. 9 and 10, pp. 214–73. Appleton-Century-Crofts, Inc., New York, 1958.

PART III

LAYING THE FOUNDATION OF ORAL COMMUNICATION

THE BEGINNINGS OF SPEECH AT HOME

Long before the child understands and uses words, a process of building his associations, memory, habits, and interpersonal relations with people important to him is supposed to take place. This invisible process serves as a foundation for his speech and for the development of his mental skills in communication.

Things and events in a conducive atmosphere in the child's family life begin to make sense to him. He learns to relate situations to his needs and to orient himself in his little world. He learns to understand how different objects work and how to manipulate them. He sizes up situations and intentions of other people and becomes alert to various occasions. He develops little strategies of his own, however elementary they may be.

It takes patience and understanding from the parents of the deaf or hard-of-hearing child to talk to him constantly, even if he does not reply, while they are playing with him. The parents must realize that it takes time to lay the foundation for his language by the continuous association of words with objects and actions.

The role of the parents cannot be duplicated. The investment of their time to establish a common experience with their hearing-impaired child is a prerequisite to his understanding of the language function and to his attempt to use words. A well-adjusted and accepted young hearing-handicapped child soon begins to notice the parents' moving lips. He associates the simple patterns of their lips with objects and with his parents' actions, gestures, and facial expressions. The child's use of his newly found language as a tool for handling situations becomes a turning point in his development.

In the beginning of speech the child is helped in a variety of ways to use his voice; he soon imitates the motion of moving lips. He becomes aware of the connection between the moving lips and vibrations which he can detect on his own and his mother's throat and cheeks. This connection is reinforced when he is able, while uttering words, to observe in the mirror the movements of his own lips and tongue and at the same time to sense these movements kinesthetically in his mouth and throat.

The child, then, enjoys the approval of his parents and the feeling of a new status gained when he begins to communicate with them orally.

To compensate for the endearing intonation of his mother's voice which a normal hearing child experiences, a hearing-impaired child should be provided an intimate atmosphere of bodily empathy. Mother's cuddling, holding the child, talking, singing, and laughing reassure him and stimulate him to vocalize.

The revealing experiences of Mrs. Shirley McArthur and Mrs. Lucille Stockman, told in their own informal words, give a picture of the intimate atmosphere in which their profoundly deaf children made their first break-through to oral communication. The conjoint efforts of these parents and the teachers and the consistent preparatory and guiding work made it possible for their deaf children later to attend regular classes successfully with hearing children in the Alhambra public schools.

SECTION 2

EXPERIENCES OF MOTHERS

"The Child's First Words"
by
Shirley McArthur[1]

1. Casual Teaching

In the process of teaching a preschool deaf child in the home to speechread and to speak, I discovered that there is a period of activity that lends itself better than any other to instruction. This is bathtime. I found myself using the bathtime more and more as a casual teaching time with Linda. There is more than one reason why this time is a most advantageous time for lessons. For one thing, a preschool child has a short attention span and a busy little pair of legs. A bathtub is a confining place. Also, a bathtub will float more things than just the soap. There are many possibilities for new words. There are boats, balls, plastic animals, and even toy furniture that can be utilized in the bathtub. The parts of the body are visible and most interesting at that time. There is something relaxing about the water and the resonance of the room. If there is some residual hearing, the mother can make full use of it in the bathroom.

The bathroom also is valuable for speechreading. Besides the hearing that is stimulated, there are the mirrors in a bathroom. Anyone who has watched a teacher of the deaf teaching speech has probably seen her use a mirror for the child to see the speech formed on the lips. Then a bit of bubblebath in the water will make all kinds of bubbles to blow. This, too, can be an important beginning for speech.

2. As Speechreading Grows

Summer vacation may seem to be a good time to slow down a bit, too busy a time for the speechreading to grow; on the contrary, this is

[1] Mrs. Shirley McArthur, of Arcadia, California, is the mother of Linda, a profoundly deaf child, now successfully attending regular classes with normal hearing children.

the time when new worlds can be opened up for the deaf child, learning about the great world of the out-of-doors. The weather is not confining now, and the child and the mother should not be confined either. Here is the opportunity to "get away from it all," if it is only a trip to the nearest park. In this, I include the parent too, because in the park the dishes are not waiting unwashed in the sink while she sits down to talk to her child, and the beds are not left unmade, haunting her in the other room. She is free with her child, and into her voice creeps a freedom of tone and into her face a relaxation of expression that she may not notice, but the bright eyes of her deaf child will see and feel. There will be more eagerness to learn, more new words with which to work. At the park or in the mountains there are rocks, flowers, trees, bugs, and birds; and at the beach there are water, sand, fish, shells, and boats; and there is time—time to explore all these wonders without the pressing duties of home. Every summer an outing missed is a golden opportunity lost both in the learning of speechreading and in the relationship of the parent to her child.

3. *When Language Begins to Form*

One of the inevitable ingredients of growing up is a knowledge of the everyday nursery rhymes and the classic children's stories, such as "The Three Little Pigs" and "Cinderella." I had a fierce determination from the beginning that somehow Linda should not miss the joy of these rhymes and stories that normal hearing children generally pick up from hearing again and again. I went to some lengths to see that she learned them and have not regretted it, as they are quite basic in the story world of a child and appear again and again in books, on television, and in plays. I can recall building a wall of blocks and breaking a real egg from the top of it in my desire to be sure she understood that nursery rhyme of "Humpty Dumpty." I used many of them on a flannel board, and can recall jumping over Jack's candle, time and again. However, the most vivid remembrance of these stories was our game of "The Three Little Pigs," which was probably the most popular of any of the stories that we acted out.

The secret of its success was its utter simplicity. Two kitchen chairs and a small children's table were the props. I happened to have three small children to be the little pigs, which turned out to be rather convenient, and I was the wolf, although we took turns having that privilege as the game progressed. The two kitchen chairs housed the little pig of the straw house and the little pig of the stick house, and the table housed the little pig of the brick house, since it was more roomy. The wolf would knock on the straw house door and say, "I want to come in." The little pig would look out, appear frightened, and say, "No, no, you can't come in." Then the wolf would huff and puff and blow the house in, and that little pig would scamper screaming to the brick house. This would be repeated at the stick house, until the three little pigs were all huddled in the brick house. There the wolf would huff and puff and not be able to blow the house in, so he would say he was going down the chimney, make a dive over the table and fall down dead on the other side—simple, but devastating to small children. The necessity of answering the wolf at the door was wonderful exercise for the use of speech, as in the excitement even the most speechless deaf child will find a voice and say something akin to "No, no, you can't come in." This sort of play brings a fuller and stronger voice, and helps the deaf child to find the desire for speech that is so necessary for a normal flow and a natural voice.

"The Child's First Words"
by
Lucille Stockman[2]

1. During All His Waking Hours

John was two years old before I began actually working with him on his speechreading. I soon saw that the lessons he received at the nursery school must be supplemented with work at home, and during all his waking hours.

[2] Mrs. Lucille Stockman, of Monrovia, California, has a profoundly deaf son, John, now attending regular classes with normal hearing children.

I suppose the first word every mother of a deaf child yearns to hear is "Mother." It was my yearning, I remember, and I was determined that this should be his first word. For almost a year, I used the word instead of the pronouns, "I" or "me"—"Mother loves you; bring Mother the paper," etc. We worked with magazine pictures of mothers and babies, and eventually John learned to speechread the word and would correctly point to the mother in the picture. One day, after a short lesson period, John pointed to the picture, then at me and said, "Mother." I shall never forget my joy as I hugged and kissed him, and he repeated, "Mother," once more for good measure. My enthusiasm at his response must have finally sealed that word in his mind.

One of John's main interests from his earliest years was cars. That was the logical word to work on next. I bought every size, color, and shape of toy car to use in our lesson. Unfortunately, John was much more interested in playing with the cars than in watching my lips, and for several months it was difficult to get more than a fleeting glance from him. I soon found that by putting the cars on the table, then moving one slowly toward my face, he followed the car with his eyes and could not help seeing the movement on my lips as I said, "This is a car. See the car. This is a red car. Give me the car. Move the car. I have a car." One day, as we were playing, John really studied my lip movements for the first time, and he repeated the word after me, which actually came out with only the vowel sound, "ah."

One of John's first adjectives was "hot." He had always shown an interest in the stove and in preparing food, so as a safety measure and a speechreading opportunity I worked diligently on the word "hot." One day while cooking, I set a hot dish aside on the stove and told him, who was standing close by, "The stove is hot. The dish is hot. Don't touch the hot dish." His little hand came toward the dish and with it the word "hot," which, of course, was only the vowel sound at this stage.

During one of John's evening baths, I was talking to him as I scrubbed off the day's dirt. The cake of soap was floating in the water, and John was playing with it. I saw the opportunity to introduce a new verb and said, "The soap floats." I took another bar of soap and showed him that it wouldn't float. "This soap doesn't float. The other soap floats." Bringing in a toy boat, I said, "The boat floats, too." The next night at bathtime when we resumed our talk about floating objects, John suddenly put the soap into the water and attempted to say, "float." To be sure he wasn't confusing the words "soap" and "float," I held the two bars in my hands and asked him which soap floats. He immediately pointed to the correct one, and again repeated the word.

A child learns a word much faster if it is an object or thing he is interested in, even though the word may be rather difficult to speech-read because of the lack of visibility on the lips. "Circus" is such a word. Speechwise, this is a stickler for deaf children because of the two "c's," one pronounced as an "s" and the other as a "k." However, since it represented such an exciting thing to John, as to most children, it seemed comparatively easy for him to learn. We read books about circuses, visited two of them, then talked about them when we got home. We had a number of small toy circus animals, and with three coffee can covers for rings we put on a little circus of our own. John put the animals through their paces, and I supplied the language: "This is a circus. These are circus animals. There are many animals in a circus. A circus is fun." After exposing him to the word in spoken and written form many, many times, in the middle of his play, I asked him to bring me the circus book. He looked quizzical at first; then when I repeated my request, he went to his book shelf and brought me the right book.

Another life situation which afforded opportunity to present a new word was the day that John's dog, Tiny, gave birth to four puppies. This is a difficult word to comprehend, and one doesn't often find an occasion which illustrates it. I was glad that the experience came to John early. I explained, "The puppies were born last night. Yesterday, Tiny didn't have any puppies. Today, she has four puppies. The puppies were born last night." By this time, John had reached the two- and three-word stage, and he added, "Tiny born puppies."

During the first two or three years, new words needed endless repetitions, perhaps a thousand times, before they became John's

own to understand and use. Now, five or six years later, I often introduce a new word saying it once or twice, writing it on the blackboard
along with the phonetic pronunciation, and have John repeat it.
Later, he will use the word spontaneously, and I know it is definitely
his. The word "president" is an example of this. "What does the president do?" he asked recently.

Even though it becomes extremely discouraging at first because
of the length of time it takes to add even one simple word to the child's
vocabulary, it is also just as rewarding when that one word is learned,
and another door of the child's understanding is opened, making him
that much closer to fitting into a hearing world.

SECTION 3

A TEACHER'S PLANNING
OF LANGUAGE EXPERIENCES
IN KINDERGARTEN

From a sheltered environment of the family, centered around
his immediate needs, the child enters school. There he has to accli-
matize to a new situation. He has to learn to cooperate in projects
and plays, do the parts assigned to him, understand the teacher and
other children, and translate his reactions into articulate phrases.

The child moves in a new orbit with new requirements and
forces. The teacher helps him to make new adjustments. As a human
engineer she helps him to fit into the group and to piece his new
experiences together so that they will make sense to him. She provides
him with a language so that he can express himself. To be able to do
so the teacher has to win the trust of the child, to establish rapport with
him, to arouse his interest, and to gain authority in his eyes. The
approval of the teacher, the acceptance by the other children, and his

desire to live up to the requirements of his new status help him to mature and to overcome his self-centeredness.

But the school cannot produce "magic" to fill out the lack of words for objects and events which the child encounters in his daily life. The parents should find time to visit the school and to become acquainted with the teacher in order to keep up with the details of their child's activities and the new vocabulary he learns in school. They should put into practice these new words and use them in their conversation with him about events at home and at school. On the other hand, the teacher should be given an opportunity to visit his home and exchange information about the child's activities with his parents.

Mrs. Jennings conducts her project, "Milk Time," with her young deaf children in a warm, friendly, and relaxed atmosphere. Skillfully, she helps the children to adjust themselves to their new environment and events. By using self-explanatory nonverbal activities, she introduces new words as they are prompted by the context of the immediate situation.

"Milk Time"
by
Cristine Jennings[1]

Concrete Language Stage

Every child learns best in an atmosphere which is warm and friendly. Especially is this relaxed climate necessary for the small deaf or hard-of-hearing child without language and speech, who is entering upon his first school experience.

The kindergarten teacher highlights the nutrition period or "Milk Time." The relaxed homelike activity of satisfying hunger and thirst provides a good emotional climate. Learning the simple language and speech involved is natural, logical, and meaningful. Since

---

[1] Mrs. Jennings is a teacher of the deaf in Alhambra, California. Her deaf children are being prepared to attend the regular classes with hearing children.

Milk Time occurs every day and is always welcomed by children and teacher, the necessary repetition of language is effected without any distasteful element of formalized drill.

The children enjoy the dramatic quality and prestige of playing out the roles. Many variations in procedure are possible, each necessitating new language to fit the occasion. Thus Milk Time may be changed spontaneously into a picnic on the grass outside, if the weather is warm. Or a child's birthday can turn Milk Time into a festive birthday party.

At special holiday periods like Christmas when tree decorations and gift making occupy much class time, Milk Time is set up in buffet style, with the children choosing at will their colored place mats, napkins, milk, and straws, and sitting informally anywhere they choose to eat.

These frequent changes of procedure and language prevent the children from becoming overly meticulous and rigid, which often happens if things are done invariably the same way every day.

Many learnings evolve from the life-situation activities surrounding Milk Time—counting, understanding and using money, learning to read their own and classmates' names and numbers, learning colors, and practicing good table manners and other social amenities. The children learn also to share attention as well as food, and to be concerned about the welfare of others. They learn to assume responsibility and to carry a task to completion.

Moreover, they learn to watch the lips for the language so essential to their activities. Their speech attempts are earnest and arise from a desire to say things properly.

Materials and Procedures

The Job Chart. The various monitor jobs are "pictured" on a large chart. The job of collecting milk money is represented by attaching to the chart one of the small cloth coin purses which all children have. The lid from a milk carton represents the job of "giving the milk." A napkin is attached for that monitor job. The child's name is slipped into the pocket alongside the job he has chosen.

"Choosing new jobs" each week provides a wonderful incentive for speech as children vie with each other for their favorite jobs.

Purses for Milk Money. Before school starts each mother is given a cloth coin purse with her child's name on it. The name is printed in large letters in India ink on "iron-on" tape which may be ironed or sewn on the purse.

Parents and child count out 25 pennies for the five days' milk. Later, as learning grows, nickels, dimes, and finally a quarter are sent.

Purses remain at school during the week and are handed out each day. Each child learns to count out his own money and hand it over to the monitor for collection. Making change, counting up the total to be ordered, and delivering the money to the cafeteria involve good learnings and the use of language.

Lunchboxes and Fruit. The lunchbox is an excellent means of transporting a piece of fruit for lunch (Milk Time), a daily news item, or an occasional toy to be shared.

Parents and child shop for the fruit and wash and pack it. At school, the names of fruit are readily learned, since all are interested in what the others have brought. Good eating habits are acquired as children learn to like all kinds of fruit from fresh fruits of every description to melons, dates, raisins, canned figs, pineapple, and applesauce. The fruit is never cut at home. There are excellent number work and good learning situations requiring the use of speech as the child learns to ask the teacher to cut his fruit and tells her how many pieces he wants.

Place Mats, Paper Napkins, and Straws. These accessories provide language opportunities as the children dispense them. The teacher accompanies the child as he makes his rounds. She speaks *for* him at first; then, when the language has meaning and he wishes to try it, she speaks *with* him. Finally, she can remain in her place, and the child will look to her for help when "stuck" for a word.

Plastic table mats come in many plain colors so that learning colors is natural and easy and requires no drill work. Paper napkins, too, are chosen for their preferred color. Holiday napkins make conversation topics with their Santa Clauses, Easter rabbits, or Thanksgiving turkeys.

Learning to drink from straws without breaking them is a good lesson in coordination as well as good tongue-and-lip exercise. Occasionally paper cups are used so children can learn to pour.

Sponges for Spills. Frequent spills occur as four-or five-year-olds learn to open their own milk cartons. One sponge is used for mopping up table tops and mats, another used to mop up the floor.

As each child finishes his lunch, he carries fruit peelings, his used napkin, and empty milk carton in the plastic mat to the wastebasket. He wipes the mat with a sponge and puts it away. Emptying this wastebasket into an outside collection can is another job which, unaccountably, is always a favorite task with children.

Examples of Simple Language. Some examples of simple language and simple speech developed from the Milk Time activities are as follows:

I brought my purse.

I have many pennies.

I have a dime. Give me change. I want two nickels.

Whose purse is this?

That's Barbara's purse (my purse, your purse).

May I take the money to the cafeteria?

We want eight milks.

Put your money in the box.

I forgot my money. May I borrow a nickel?

It's time for milk. I washed my hands.

May I give the mats (or napkins, straws, milk)?

What color mat do you want?

I want a yellow mat.

Here's your straw.

Take your milk, Helen. Thank you, John. You're welcome, Helen.

Mother and I made cookies for everybody.

My banana is spoiled. Cut it off.

Watch me! (Child soon insists that he be watched as he speaks.)

Sit with me! (Small spontaneous conversation develops as children pair off.)

Cut my apple. I want six pieces. Cut out the seeds.

Move over, please.

I spilled my milk. Help me!

John is not polite.

May we have a picnic outside?

I have a pear. What do you have?

I'm full. May I take this piece (of apple) home?

I finished my milk and banana.

John finished first. I'm second.

Tomorrow I will bring cupcakes for everybody.

Barbara bumped me. Sit down, Barbara.

Today is Friday. We take our purses home.

Bibliography

Ewing, Irene R., and A. W. G. Ewing. *The Handicap of Deafness*. Longmans, Green & Co., Ltd., London, 1938.

Fiedler, Miriam Foster. *Deaf Children in a Hearing World*. The Ronald Press Company, New York, 1952.

John Tracy Clinic Correspondence Course for Parents of Little Deaf Children, 2–5 years of age. 806 W. Adams Blvd., Los Angeles 18, California.

Lassman, Grace H. *Language for the Preschool Deaf Child*. Grune & Stratton, Inc., New York, 1950.

McCarthy, Dorothea. "Language Development in Children," *Manual of Child Psychology and Education*. John Wiley & Sons, Inc., New York, 1956.

Pauls, Miriam, and William G. Hardy. "Hearing Impairment in Preschool Age Children," *Laryngoscope*, 63:534, (June) 1953.

PART IV

ORAL COMMUNICATION ON THE CONCRETE CONCEPTUAL LEVEL

THE WORLD WIDENED, GENERALIZED, AND DIFFERENTIATED BY THE CHILD

The hearing-impaired child in the primary grades is introduced into a wider world by the development of a new dimension of language and by an enlarged background of experience. In an environment of new experiences, structured by the teacher, he finds a new orientation. He learns to comprehend events around him in terms of past, present, and future. He handles objects in terms of their location, qualities, measurement, and number. He classifies the specific objects he encounters into general terms and group words.

New forces and motivations enter into his life and activate his adjustment to new conditions. He wants to be socially acceptable. He learns to adhere to the rules of the game and to follow the norms of his new group in school and on the playground. He finds that these norms apply to him, and that ideas of fair play mean sharing things alike. His new values and allegiances are reinforced in a new language of slogans, commands, and admonitions.

In Mrs. Rose Pissakov's report of her experience in teaching deaf children, she makes use of such devices as the calendar and other instructional materials often used during the child's primary grade. Her insight into the growing minds of the children and her close contact with them have helped her to lead children successfully from the world of direct, immediate experiences into the vicarious world at large.

SECTION 2

INTRODUCING CONCEPTS OF TIME AND SPACE
(Primary Grade)[1]

by

Rose Pissakov[2]

Basis for Oral Communication

As a part of a social group in the kindergarten, the child is given a job in a class project and has to assume a responsibility. The child is motivated to live up to the expectations of the teacher and of the other children, and to the requirements of the situation in the project.

At the same time, he is given words for things and actions. He learns that lip movements have a meaning and that he has to watch the mouth to get this meaning. He also learns to imitate these movements with voice in order to make himself understood.

Broadening of Social and Language Concepts in the First Grade

A child is made more conscious and sensitive to his behavior in relation to the feelings of others. He is taught behavior and appearance that will make him more socially acceptable, for example:

1. We do not walk in front of people, we walk behind them.
2. If we must walk in front, we say, "Pardon me!"

[1] Mrs. Pissakov's deaf children are being prepared to attend the regular classes with hearing children.

[2] Rose Pissakov is a teacher of the deaf in the Alhambra, California, public schools. She has profited greatly in her skill as a teacher from her own experience with her profoundly deaf son, Stanley. Stanley's success in school and in advanced studies and his ability as a public speaker are the results of his mother's patient and competent work with him, as well as his own unflagging efforts. Stanley had no difficulty in keeping up with his hearing contemporaries in public school, and later excelled in his studies in junior college where he received a degree of associate of arts. He is now continuing his studies toward a B.S. degree in industrial design at Art Center, Los Angeles, California.

3. When somebody talks, we watch and wait; we do not interrupt.

4. We have good table manners—we take little bites, and we do not shout.

The child's use of concrete and abstract concepts of language should grow from life situations which are created by the teacher or which develop naturally in a given situation. The teacher should not use artificially irrelevant words that are not connected with the situation which occupies the children at the moment.

Classroom Procedure and Techniques

The Calendar. The use of the calendar helps the child to understand that events are taking place in time—day after day, week after week, month after month—and conveys to him the idea of the past, present, and future. A large calendar (approximate size 36 in. by 48 in.) is made from tagboard placed over chip board. The pockets are formed by creasing the tagboard and fastening it down with paper fasteners. The date, weather, month, and year cards are removable.

The calendar is placed on the blackboard ledge. Each child has calendar duty for one week. He is questioned by the teacher while the others observe. As he answers her questions, he places the appropriate date and weather cards in the proper pockets. Some typical questions are as follows:

What day was yesterday? Yesterday was . . . .
What day is today? Today is . . . .
What month is it? This is . . . .
What is the date? It is . . . . (We introduce ordinals in relation to dates, etc.)
What year is it? This is . . . .
What day will tomorrow be? Tomorrow will be . . . .
What is the weather?
The sun is shining. The sun is shining brightly.
It is a clear day. It is a beautiful day.

The following are typical outgrowths from the calendar related to the possible experiences of the various children. We learn there are special days, such as birthdays, Valentine's Day, Hallowe'en, etc. There are also holidays, such as Thanksgiving, Christmas, Easter. Special days are just days to remember, but holidays are not only to be remembered but we stay at home and are absent from school.

We learn to anticipate holidays in terms of units of time, such as:

How many more days to . . . ?
How many more weeks to . . . ?
How many more months to . . . ?

We learn about the seasons, namely, that certain groups of months fall under certain seasons and each season has certain characteristics. Below is a chart serving as a visual aid for the four seasons.

Chart of the Four Seasons

Days	*Months*	*Seasons*
	DECEMBER	
	JANUARY	WINTER
SUNDAY	FEBRUARY	
MONDAY	MARCH	
	APRIL	SPRING
TUESDAY	MAY	
WEDNESDAY	JUNE	
	JULY	SUMMER
THURSDAY	AUGUST	
FRIDAY	SEPTEMBER	
	OCTOBER	AUTUMN
SATURDAY	NOVEMBER	

In relation to the seasons, we learn about the temperature. In winter it is cold; in summer, hot; in spring and autumn, cool; etc. A thermometer is hung outside the door of the schoolhouse, and the children observe the daily rise and fall of temperature. The teacher can construct a thermometer. The face is drawn on tagboard, which is attached to stiff chip board. The mercury is represented by a red ribbon sewn to a white ribbon and drawn through top and bottom of the board. It can be raised and lowered by the children according to the temperature of the day.

We learn that temperature means hot or cold, that the thermometer shows how high or low the temperature is, that the lines are called degrees and are steps to show the temperature. We learn the shades of difference in temperature—hot, cold, cool, warm. We also learn comparisons of degree of temperature, such as colder than, warmer than. Questions are asked as follows:

What is the temperature today? The temperature is . . . degrees.

What was the temperature yesterday? The temperature was . . . degrees.

Is it warm? Hot? Cool? Etc.

Yesterday the temperature was . . . degrees, and today the temperature is . . . degrees. Which is warmer? Which is cooler? Which day was warmer? Cooler?

Yesterday was warmer than today.

In relation to the seasons we learn what happens to the plants and trees, and to animals. We learn what we wear and do in the different seasons. The teacher shows well-illustrated books to the children and asks questions pertaining to the various phases of the seasons.

At the Store. In our classroom we have a grocery store composed of a counter, a canopy, and shelves. Each shelf box contains a different category of food. Over each shelf box hangs the name of the category and a price.

The teacher picks up a can of vegetables or fruit and asks: "Is this a can of fruit or a can of vegetables?" The children answer accordingly and place the can on the proper shelf.

As they play store the teacher helps them to express in words what they want and how much it costs.

I want a can of . . . .
I want a box of . . . .
How much does . . . . cost?
I want a carton of . . . .
I want a sack of . . . .

Later the teacher explains meanings of pint, quart, dozen, etc. A quart holds four cups. A pint holds two cups. A dozen eggs are 12 eggs. A measuring cup may be used for measuring objects and counting them.

A toy cash register and scales provide opportunity for children to weigh and pay for the food in the store.

ILLUSTRATION OF SHELF BOXES IN THE STORE

FRUIT	JUICES	CEREAL
20¢	15¢	30¢

VEGETABLES	EGGS	BUTTER	MILK
25¢	60¢	40¢	15¢

SECTION 3

CLASSROOM ACTIVITIES OF CHILDREN
by
Mildred A. Groht[1] and Norma Harris

Children who are interested, alert, and happy will find their days crowded with "things to do" and will want to talk about them. The wise teacher will make use of every opportunity provided by the

[1] These introductory sentences were supplied by Mildred Groht, Ed.D., who is principal of the Lexington School for the Deaf, New York City, which is one of the pioneer schools of oral education in the United States. Dr. Groht has emphasized in her long career as a teacher of the deaf the experiential approach to teaching language arts in many articles and in her new book, *Natural Language for Deaf Children* (Volta Bureau, Washington, D.C., 1958).

children. All activities of children should be used as a basis for work in the language arts—speechreading, writing, speaking, and reading. The following accounts of classroom events are instances of the type of speechreading and language usage that go on day after day.

A Party
by
Norma Harris[2]

The opportunity of such a typical experience as a birthday party provides the deaf children with phrases and expressions commonly used at such an event.

Jean's Birthday Party

A. Plans for the party were discussed by the teacher and the children.
   1. We discussed what day to have the party and the hour.
   2. Made a list of:
      foods for party
      party supplies
      games to be played
      people to be invited
   3. Wrote a letter to Jean's mother giving her our list of things to be bought and brought.
   4. Wrote to or orally invited members of the staff.
B. Before the party.
   1. Children straightened the room.
   2. Children washed their hands and combed their hair.
   3. Mother and teacher prepared the table.
C. The party.
   1. Jean welcomed each guest at the door, invited them in, and received their happy birthday wishes.

[2] Norma Harris, M.A., is a teacher of the deaf, Lexington School for the Deaf, New York.

2. Children talked about candy, cake, and favors found on the table. All put on paper hats.
3. Mother lighted the candles. Jean blew them out.
4. All children sang "Happy Birthday."
5. Cake and Coca-Cola were served.
6. Games were played:
   donkey game
   chair game
   guessing game
   blowing balloons
7. Favors and toys were given to each child to take home.

D. Tired, happy children said good-by and happy birthday to Jean and thank you to mother and Jean.

A Letter to David
by
Norma Harris

A. David's absence from school was observed.
   1. David's two-day absence was discussed—what might be wrong?
   2. The decision was made to phone his mother to find out.
   3. Class discussed David's illness with the mumps, how long he must be absent, how he feels, and what each can do to cheer him.
B. Writing a group letter.
   1. Group suggested things to tell David and questions to ask him.
   2. Children dictated a letter to the teacher.
   3. Children drew pictures to enclose in the letter.
   4. Children found out where David lived and addressed the envelope.
C. Trip to mailbox to mail letter (with discussion about what happens to a letter from mailbox until delivery).
D. Discussion of David's possible reactions to letter.

E. David's return to school, with letter. He tells of mother bringing
   it to him and his feelings. (Children repeat discussion of letter's
   trip from mailbox to post office, via mailman to mother.) He
   comments on statements in letter and answers questions.

Section 4

COMMUNICATION IN GAMES
AND ON EXCURSIONS

A hearing-impaired child must be kept active and must be given
many opportunities to counter his tendencies toward withdrawal and
physical and mental passivity. Participation in well-planned games
is an important means for developing spontaneous oral communication, resourcefulness, and quick thinking. An excursion to the zoo
with careful preparation and the use of the experience for discussing
the trip is one of many stimulating projects which can stir the imagination of the child.

Mrs. Mary Ann Strakosch prepares her hard-of-hearing children
to attend regular classes and to play with hearing children. She de-
scribes games and a trip to the zoo and dramatizes them in words she
uses in such situations. She guards against excessive repetition or
stereotyped phraseology, varying and supplementing her expressions
and words in order to develop flexibility and a better vocabulary in
the children.

SECTION 5

GAMES AND A TRIP TO THE ZOO
by
Mary Ann Strakosch[1]

1. Circle Game

The Guessing Bottle. The children sit in a circle on the rug. One of the children takes his place in the center with a bottle. He spins the bottle. When the bottle stops spinning and the neck points to one of the children in the circle, the player asks the child a question, "Who has brown eyes?" etc. Then that child must answer and automatically becomes IT, taking his place in the center and repeating the cycle.

The Color Game. The children sit in a circle. The teacher gives them the vocabulary of various colors—red, blue, green, yellow, black, etc.—and demonstrates the game by saying: "I see something black in this room; what is it?" The teacher has in mind an object that is black, and the children must try to guess what this object is. They say: "Is it the blackboard?" "Is it the book?" "Is it Billy's shoes?" When the correct answer is given, the child guessing it becomes IT. All children like to play this game, which is very beneficial for speechreading and language development.

The Animal Game. The children sit in a circle, and the teacher gives the vocabulary of various farm animals (dog, cat, horse, pig, cow, lamb, duck, chickens, etc.) and then the animals from the zoo (bear, moose, lion, camel, bobcat, elephant, zebra, monkey, tiger). One child asks a question, for example, "What likes milk and purrs?" The child guessing correctly asks another question in his turn. "What has a loud bark?" (Dog.) "What animal is small and likes to swim?" (Duck.) "What animals in the zoo are yellow?" (Lion, tiger, bobcat.) "What is the largest animal of all?" (Elephant.) Etc. In this way the children learn a great deal about animals and what they do.

[1] Mrs. Mary Ann Strakosch, A.B., is a teacher of the hard of hearing in the day classes, public schools, Pasadena, California.

The teacher can elaborate upon this game. She may ask a child to do something, for example: "Act like a bear." Then the child may select someone and say: "Whoever this points to is a 'monkey.'" Then, after the child has done the imitation, he selects still another and says: "You are an elephant."

New interests, curiosity, and imagination are aroused in children by visits to museums, aquariums, zoos, airports, railroad stations, and the like. The children, however, should be thoroughly prepared for these trips in advance, and their experience of the excursion should be utilized in the classroom to build up oral communication, skills, and knowledge of everyday life. The children should be encouraged to make investigations on their own. The parents may help their children connect their experiences as they view educational motion pictures and television shows together.

2. A Trip to the Zoo

An essential part of the value of the excursion is the preparation before going on a trip to the zoo. The teacher should first connect the previous experiences of the children at a zoo by asking the class questions: "Have you ever been to a zoo?" "What animals did you see?" The children respond by telling the names of some of the animals familiar to them—lions, monkeys, elephants.

Then the teacher says, "We are going to the zoo on Wednesday." They will leave the school at 9:30 A.M. on the school bus. The children are to bring their own lunches and will have a picnic at the park. While riding on the bus, the teacher and the children discuss what their behavior will be at the zoo. Some of the questions children may ask on the bus: "Can we feed the animals?" "Will we see snakes?" "I hope we will see a giraffe." "Can we ride the ponies?" The teacher should be well prepared with answers.

At the zoo, the children and the teacher discuss the various animals they see. Some remarks are brought out by the children as they pass from cage to cage. "The camel has only one hump." "The monkey wants some peanuts." "Where do the elephant and polar bear come from?"

The teacher tells the children the names of the animals they see: the buffalo, king snake, rattlesnake, penguins, raccoon, dog, mink, the seals.

Later, at school the children may discuss their "Day at the Zoo." The teacher puts the list of animals on the board as the children tell her the names: penguins, elephants, lions, tigers, monkeys, kangaroo, water buffalo, zebra, polar bear, brown bear, black bear, snakes.

The children may write stories about what they saw at the zoo, and each child reads his story to the class. For an art lesson the children may paint pictures and make clay animals. The children may play a game related to their trip to the zoo by sitting in a circle on the floor in the classroom. Each child imitates an animal he saw at the zoo. The child says, "Guess what I am." The class must guess the name of the animal that is being imitated.

Section 6

UTILIZING RESIDUAL HEARING IN SIMPLE SITUATIONS
(In School)

A child who can distinguish the fragments of speech sounds can be trained by a skillful teacher to associate these fragments with the visual-kinesthetic-rhythmic pattern of the word or sentence. These fragments of hearing are associated in training with (1) visible movements of the speaker's lips, (2) rhythm of the spoken words which the child senses, and (3) the child's growing awareness of the kinesthetic sensations of his own lips, tongue, and glottal movements.

The child understands the sentence better when he finds the key words which help to complete the sentence, by using all available situational and sensory cues. This ability to get the meaning of the whole from key words must be trained and can be improved by a knowledge of language, which is fortified by experience gained in life situations.

The following demonstration reported by Miss Rosalin D. Loughran is based on simple situations and illustrates one of many possible forms and techniques of auditory training combined with speechreading. Miss Loughran's demonstration is described in expressions which she found effective with her pupils, all of whom had various degrees of hearing losses. They were students of a residential school.

SECTION 7

THE USE OF GROUP HEARING AIDS IN CLASSROOM TEACHING
(With Children from Eight to Nine)
by
Rosalin D. Loughran[1]

The Purpose of the Demonstration

It was intended to demonstrate that hearing-handicapped children can be trained to use whatever residual hearing they may possess to improve their speech, increase their language development, and accelerate their educational growth when consistent auditory training is combined with speechreading.

The four children chosen for the demonstration were eight or nine years of age and had completed their third year in school. Audio-

[1] This demonstration was presented at the Summer Meeting, Alexander Graham Bell Association for the Deaf, Los Angeles, in 1957. Miss Rosalin D. Loughran, M.A., is a teacher of the deaf at the California School for the Deaf, Riverside, California. She is a former student of Dr. and Mrs. A. W. G. Ewing, Manchester University, Manchester, England.

grams projected on the screen showed that the children had differing patterns of hearing loss. Two were able to identify some connected speech through hearing alone. Another child could identify some speech sounds. The fourth child could identify some gross sounds and rhythms, but was unable to identify speech. She was not required to close her eyes when exercises for discrimination of speech were used.

During their three years in a residential school these children had been exposed consistently to a program of amplification. They were expected to reply orally and in sentences.

Materials and Procedure

1. Three pictures showing children walking, running, and skipping; also a record having the rhythms of walking, running, and skipping.

The teacher shows the picture and asks: "What is this girl doing?"

The child replies: "She is walking."

One child walks, and the others clap the rhythm. The music for walking is played. The children listen and clap the rhythm.

The same procedure is followed for pictures of running and skipping. The children listen to the music and distinguish between a walk, a run, a skip, and answer orally in sentences. "That was walking," etc.

2. Three flash cards with words, cow, rabbit, and elephant, are shown.

The teacher shows the word cow and asks: "What is this word?" "How many syllables are in this word?" She encourages conversation about the animal. "What is a cow?" "Where would you see a cow?" etc. She proceeds in the same manner with the words, rabbit and elephant. Then the children listen and distinguish between the words, cow, rabbit, and elephant. The children answer orally and in sentences, "I saw the rabbit."

3. Three flash cards are shown with the questions: "How are you?" "How old are you?" "What day is today?"

The child reads the first question and answers it. He also tells how many syllables or counts are in the question. Children repeat the question and clap the rhythm. They proceed in the same manner with the two remaining questions. Then the children listen, and the teacher asks one of the questions.

4. Three pictures are displayed: A boy watering some flowers. A girl blowing bubbles. A boy eating some watermelon.

They discuss each picture. The children are encouraged to talk about each picture. There is a boy in the picture. He is watering some flowers. They place pictures in a chart. The children watch and listen. Teacher says: "There is a girl in the picture. She is blowing bubbles." The child finds the right picture and repeats the description.

SECTION 8

AWARENESS AND USE OF RHYTHM

The awareness of rhythm helps hearing-impaired children to compensate for their hearing deficiency and contributes to the improvement of their voice and speech. This awareness helps them to imitate speech and to speechread better. They learn to recognize patterns of purposive speech, regularities in intonation, accents, emphases, and breath pauses. These patterns they sense from multisensory experiences, such as auditory (from remnants of hearing),[1] visual (from movements of lips), kinesthetic (from "feeling" words in their mouth),[2] as well as tactile (from feeling the vibration of playing the piano and the vibration of the floor produced by playing

---

[1] Recognition of speech rhythm and of patterns of voice intonation as well as of phonemes and groups of phonemes are essential discriminative and interpretive functions of the brain which are gained by an "audiological education" of the deaf child with various degrees of deafness (H. C. Huizing, 1959).

[2] F. and Grace Heider, 1941.

various musical instruments).[3] They develop correct respiration and learn to control the muscles of their tongue and other speech organs.

The use of rhythm helps the modulation of their voices and combats the tendency to speak in a monotone, with its characteristic flatness. Development of the sense of rhythm is correlated with auditory training and speech exercises, and with rhythmic movements of the body in dances and games. Choric speech, singing in unison, recital of nursery rhymes, jingles, verses, sayings, and familiar expressions are useful. The sense of rhythm is also trained while dramatizing stories with bits of conversation. It is further trained by repeated showings of special films[4] with the close-ups of the dialogues of the film characters.

Constant application of the rhythm of spoken words is supported by the clapping of hands or by musical beats. Thus, gradually, the sense of verbal rhythm becomes instilled or "internalized" in the child. In using the expression of one of the musicians,[5] this internalized rhythm becomes a sort of "inner metronome" for the child. The rhythm of the word reverberates in him and in his muscles by empathy.

The rhythmic sense of speech is supported in learning by the expressive movements of the speakers, such as their gestures, postures, and the movements of their facial muscles. As the child's proficiency in language grows, his increased verbal sense of rhythm helps him to recognize the correct order and regularity of grammatical and syntactic forms and structures.

[3] Suggestions for useful rhythmic exercises can be found in the book of Margaret S. Kent, 1938.

[4] See Part VII, "Intensive Training in Speechreading with Life Situation Films."

[5] Mr. Thurston Knutsen.

SECTION 9

DANCE PROGRAM FOR THE HEARING-IMPAIRED CHILD

by

Jeri Salkin and Trudi Schoop[1]

The all-pervasive pattern of life, from its beginning to its end, is movement—movement and rhythm. And rhythms are as varied and as numerous as individual living beings.

Not only does man take part in the basic rhythm of life, he is part of it. His own rhythm expresses itself in his way of walking, of moving about, of inhaling and exhaling, and in his pattern of bodily tension and release.

Dance is movement in rhythm; it is movement we can see, movement we can feel.

Dance has been used for many years in many ways. Since prehistoric times, man has used movement and rhythm and music to express his feelings. Through movement, primitive man expressed love and hate, fear and supplication, anger and wonder.

Before a baby can speak he uses movement to communicate and express himself. Movement is the most basic and most universally understood form of communication.

Each of us starts life with our own inborn traits and characteristics, and we are able to preserve our individuality, despite the impacts of culture, through the inherent mechanism of maturation. Although each individual must do his own growing at his own learning rate, we all normally pass through the same physical developmental patterns. These patterns include the movements of head and eyes, the movements of hands opening and closing, gripping and grasping, picking and plucking, the legs kicking, and the body twisting, crawling, rocking, and walking. This pattern is true, in essence, even for the handicapped.

---

[1] Dance therapists, The John Tracy Clinic, Los Angeles, California.

These basic physical movements of childhood are developed, varied, and combined as we use them throughout life to express ourselves. We use them to communicate. We use them when we work and play. We use them to express our emotional feelings. We also use them to accentuate our speech. The highest refinement of these movements is seen when we watch the intricate combinations of movements in rhythm performed by the trained dancer.

In order to teach rhythm and dance to the hearing-impaired child, it is important that one knows about and understands this normal pattern of physical development. Modern dance, which is the basis of our technique, is based on these fundamental movements.

The objective of our dance program for the hearing-handicapped is to help develop control and coordination, physical and emotional balance, and to broaden the sense of rhythm. The physically and emotionally well-balanced person feels confident to express himself and to communicate with others. And although the hearing-impaired may not be able completely to master control of speech rhythms, it is possible for them to develop confidence and control in physical movement.

It is important for the hearing-impaired to find an outlet for expression; it is also important that their individual rhythm be developed and guided. In addition, it is necessary that they know about and learn to move the various parts of their bodies.

In teaching dance to the hearing-impaired, we have two approaches. From a physical standpoint, we try to teach them to be aware of and to move isolated parts of the body, such as the head, the shoulders, the arms, the legs, and the hands. We teach through the use of imitation. We move and they follow. We say the word that designates the part of the body being used and we follow this with the word that signifies the action, for example, we give them, "Head: up-down," or "side-side," or "around and around," "Shoulders: up-down, up-down," and so forth. The words are continually repeated as the movement is performed. By isolating the various parts of the body in this way they move their arms, hands, legs, feet, head, and torso.

They are given stretches for suppleness and also to broaden their movement range: front, back, and lateral stretches, and bends and swings. Combinations of movements are extended in space in all directions. Strength building exercises are given: abdominal lifts (lying on floor and rising to sitting position), deep knee bends, arch lifts, kicks, and jumps.

For posture alignment we not only demonstrate but we actually move each individual into a harmonious body balance. Then they try to maintain this good posture when performing other movements such as sitting, walking, running.

For full body control, we give coordinated movements. These may be combinations of several movements which make use of various qualities of movement.

These exercises of body awareness and control are the fundamental part of every lesson from the beginning classes to the advanced. And throughout all of these exercises we emphasize rhythm and quality and the relationship of language.

To develop a balance between the two most extreme positions: the closed-in and the opened-out, the class is given several variations of these two positions. For example, an exercise may start with "Eyes: open-close," then, "Mouth: open-close," "Hands: open-close," "Arms and shoulders: open-close," "The whole body: open-close." And again, we use the words "open-close" as we do the movement.

It is necessary and also enjoyable, regardless of age, to learn and repeat some of the basic movements of childhood such as the gallop, the skip, the hop, the jump, and the turn. The age level and the degree of advancement determine the amount of variation in quality and tempo, the simplicity and complexity of movement, and the degree of control demanded.

The second part of our teaching approach deals with the emotions. We call upon their normal emotions and we stimulate the creative expression of these emotions by using a physical approach. That is, we teach the movements most often used to express these emotions: for example, the raised shoulder, the gasp, and the nervous run which are often seen in fear, or the clenched fist or stamping foot used in anger, and the clapping of hands and twirling and jumping we often see in joy. By first imitating the movement and experiencing the emotion, it can be easier for the hearing-impaired to understand the meaning of the related word when they do learn to say it. By being able to relate the word with the expression, they are able to give it a more accurate rhythmic quality.

Scarfs and other props are used to help vary the quality of movement, such as staccato, legato, heavy, and light. We teach them to control themselves in space: up and down, lateral forward and backward. They learn floor patterns such as the circular, diagonal, straight and curved lines.

To help them feel the rhythmic beat, we use drums and stick beaters. We have them clap their hands, slap the floor, and stamp their feet. Individual rhythm as well as group participation is encouraged. Because it is possible in dance to give rhythm a visual form, we can teach the hearing-impaired child rhythms other than his own.

Children are encouraged to count aloud as they beat. We teach them the basic measure structures, such as 2/4, 3/4, 4/4, and 6/8. And they seem to enjoy varying the accent. The rhythmic beat is used in combinations with walking while beating the drum or clapping the hands. Tempos are varied with sudden stops interrupting fast runs. Contrasting tempos of fast and slow are followed in rhythmic beat and in movement. Learning to control these rhythmic movement qualities can aid the quality and rhythm of speech.

Our dance program stimulates the emotional and physical feelings and in this way increases the desire to communicate through language. It helps make a social contact and it encourages recognition of others and group participation.

This approach to teaching the hearing-impaired has been successful not only in classwork but also in the performing of dance programs. In one instance, preschool children, two to six years of age, interpreted the Christmas story in dance. By imitating and repeating the simple movements needed to portray the characters, these children were able to understand the characters and perform for an audience. Each group learned the movements of the characters they were portraying—Mary, Joseph, the Three Wise Men, the innkeeper, the shepherds, angels, and stars—and they also learned their stage cues. The performance proved most enjoyable not only for the young children but also for the audience of parents and friends.

Whether we are teaching children or adults, we call upon the basic movement forms of life. We call upon the basic emotional feelings of life. We call upon the rhythm of life. We use these movements, emotions, and rhythms in making a social contact. We use them to help develop what is already there, and we use them to guide the students into a framework of control, balance, and true freedom of expression through dance.

Bibliography

Fry, D. B., and E. Whetnall. "The Auditory Approach in the Training of Deaf Children," *Lancet*, 2:583, 1954.

Groht, Mildred. *Natural Language for Deaf Children*. Volta Bureau, Washington, D.C., 1958.

Hardy, W. G. "Hearing Aids for Deaf Children," *Volta Review*, 56:355, 1954.

Heider, F., and Grace Heider. "Studies in Psychology of the Deaf," No. 2, *Psychological Monographs*, 53:1–158, 1941.

Huizing, H. C. "Deaf-Mutism—Modern Trends in Treatment and Prevention," *Advances in Oto-Rhino-Laryngology*, 5:74–106, 1959. (S. Karger, Basel/New York.)

Hudgins, C. V. "Auditory Training: Its Possibilities and Limitations," *Volta Review*, 56:339, 1954.

Keaster, Jacqueline. "Impaired Hearing," in Wendell Johnson, *Speech Handicapped Children*. Harper & Brothers, New York, 1948.

Kent, Margaret S. *Suggestions for Teaching Rhythm to the Deaf*. Frederick, Maryland, 1938.

Neiman, L. V. (ed.). *Residual Hearing of Deaf and Hard of Hearing Children*. Academy of Pedagogical Sciences, Moscow, 1957.

PART V

TRANSITION
TO ABSTRACT LANGUAGE

ACQUIRING A CULTURAL HERITAGE

As a hearing-impaired child advances in maturity, new barriers may seem to hamper him in mastering the language which is essential to his understanding of concepts that are the foundation of his cultural heritage. Without such mastery, he cannot enter fully into social and economic life or understand the reasoning and thinking which are basic to science. Abstract words and metaphors, words indicating relationship or those which have several meanings, the grasp of language principles used in compound grammatical sentences with subordinate clauses, all are difficult for him. His advancement in language, thinking and knowledge must be continually reinforced and vitalized.

The world at large should be brought vividly and interestingly to the classroom by the teachers who use visual aids, school projects, and exhibits.

The materials and facts are not presented to the child disconnectedly. He is helped to relate various phenomena of learning. He questions the causes of events and reasons out their consequences. The teacher's explanations and the information he finds in books become a part of his own thought processes.

In his development, he may assume a new active attitude which will help him to reach new levels of understanding. Each new attainment brings new attitudes which, with the help of teachers and parents, elevate his level of understanding and initiative.

In the desire to prepare himself for his future active role in the hearing society, he may learn to use his own efforts to seek out situations which will enrich his knowledge and contacts. He may begin consciously to strive to improve his speech and language, to learn how to study effectively and how to get along with hearing people.

The classroom teacher, in setting the stage for the child's transition to reasoning in terms of abstract concepts, must prepare the child carefully for a desire to use a new language—the language of abstraction.

Section 2

USING AUDIOVISUAL AIDS ON ALL GRADE LEVELS

In order to make abstract concepts meaningful to a hearing-impaired child, a creative teacher should take special pains to build these concepts for him by using concrete, actional, and vivid images through liberal use of visual aids. His cumulative experiences in observing and participating in experiments and educational games give the child a grasp of the relationships and connectedness of things and phenomena in nature and in human life.

In this way, he learns to follow the continuity of what he reads and to relate these meanings with those learned from the lips of speakers. The words in sentences and paragraphs tie together into a continuous meaning. The words are imbued with images and with an evocative power which bring to his mind his past experiences and knowledge previously acquired. This ability stimulates the child's interest in reading and in joining in conversations and discussions.

Audiovisual aids and equipment make valuable contributions for teaching hearing-impaired children of all grade levels. The use of these aids for these children is even more important than for the hearing children.

Miss Miriam Keslar and the speech staff of the Los Angeles City Schools use a variety of audiovisual aids for the speech improvement of children with slight hearing impairment who are attending speech-correction classes in the Los Angeles City Elementary Schools. These aids and techniques are also helpful in teaching speechreading to hard-of-hearing children.

The two lessons which are presented here, "Color" and "Farm Animals," have been supplemented by ideas and materials from students attending a seminar conducted by Dr. Janet Jeffers, Los Angeles State College.

SECTION 3

AUDIOVISUAL AIDS IN WORK WITH COLOR

by
Miriam Keslar[1]

Building a curriculum on very realistic grounds for deaf and hard-of-hearing children requires that teachers make each day's work as interesting, varied, and meaningful as possible. In work with color, a wide variety of stimulating instructional aids is available for use in building the child's language of color.

Finding Materials

One of the major problems is to find enough interesting materials, techniques, and procedures to give the child stimulating repetitions for learning skills and for development of language. However, many new and varied visual aids are on the market today. Local industries

---

[1] Supervisor of speech correction, Los Angeles City Schools.

and organizations are often excellent sources of free material. Many of them produce attractive and colorful materials which can be used in a variety of ways. Teachers will want to continue to create their own materials for specific needs of children.

It is important, at all levels, to find more and better ways to teach children to work independently. Many of the materials included here will make it possible for children to occupy themselves gainfully.

Audiovisual aids are devised to supplement good teaching, and to shorten the process of learning. Their use reduces loss of learning, increases interest, stimulates thinking and observing, and makes lessons come alive for deaf and hard-of-hearing children.

Presentation of Materials, Lessons, and Stories

In the presentation of materials, lessons, and stories the teacher strives for ease, naturalness, fluency, poise, and animation. All these are essential to effective presentation. When mastered, these attributes add immeasurably to the pleasure and value of the work.

Among the most valuable audiovisual tools are the following:

Educational games	Records
Educational toys	Slides
Exhibits	Slot charts
Flannel boards	Stereoscopes
Microphones	Still films
Motion pictures	Story boards
Pegboards	Study pictures
Puppets	Tape recorders
Radios	Telephone kits
Record players	Television

The following lessons have been planned for the purpose of emphasizing the use of audiovisual aids in instruction. It is hoped that this material will serve as a source of suggestions to teachers and, in turn, of pleasant learning experiences for children.

Let's Talk about Color. Color is in nearly everything we see. It is here presented in varying ways so that it will be made a part of each day's classroom experience. Stories, games, and color experiences develop understanding at various age levels and make for continuity of pupil growth.

Ways for Learning about Color

1. Know and use the colors by name. Find out about the spectrum. Know the colors in sequence.
2. Know that colors can be changed through mixing. Know how to mix new colors in paint or crayon. Know how to lighten colors in paint or crayon. Know how to darken colors in paint or crayon.
3. Recognize related colors.
4. Distinguish a bright color from a dull color.
5. Be able to do simple color matching.
6. Know and use a color vocabulary:

rainbow colors	dark colors
bright colors	light colors
dull colors	warm colors
related colors	cool colors

Educational Games

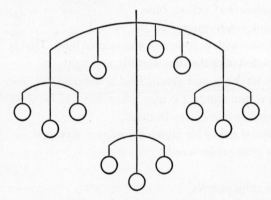

A color mobile will add interest and will furnish a continued source of delight as children watch it catch the light and turn quietly on the slightest movement of air.

The color mobile utilizes colored plastic disks attached by nylon threads to an aluminum crossbar and three fine piano wires. Perfect balance is established by adjusting the length of the threads and their positions on the crossbar.

The 18-in. aluminum crossbar is made from ⅛-in. aluminum wire curved slightly. The piano wires are 6 in. in length; and the plastic disks are 2¼ in. in diameter. A small hole is made in each disk with a hot needle or small nail, and the disks are attached to the wires with white or black nylon thread. The mobile is suspended from the ceiling or from a wall bracket.

The three disks attached to the aluminum crossbar represent the three primary colors—yellow, blue, and red. The disks hanging from the piano wires represent the secondary colors. The three below the primary yellow disk are blue-green, green, and yellow-green. The three below the primary blue disk are red-violet, violet, and blue-violet. The three below the primary red disk are yellow-orange, orange, and red-orange.

The Spectrum. Place a prism on a table or suspend it near a window where the sunlight will fall on it. Talk about the prism, observe it, and see how the sunlight passing through a glass prism will form a series of colors called a spectrum and how we see many hues in the spectrum.

Spectral colors: violet, blue, green, yellow, orange, red.

Basic or primary colors: red, yellow, blue.

Neutral colors: black, white, gray.

Warm colors are those with yellow, red, and orange hues. That is because they are associated with the sun, warmth, and light.

Cool colors are violet, blue, and green. That is because they are associated with air, sky, and water. (Warm colors seem to be close to us, and cool colors seem to move away from us.)

Use squares of colored paper for giving the names of colors.

Use flash cards for giving color words.

Speechreading:

Aloud: "This is the color purple."

"This is the word that says purple."

"Watch me now and read what I say."

Silent: "This is the color purple."
"This is the word that says purple."
Use this pattern for presenting each color word.

A Color Top. Large color tops are available in toy stores. They have clear plastic domes through which one can see the colors as they change when the top is spinning. This provides interesting conversation.

A Color Table. Arrange a small table with many objects emphasizing one certain color. For example, the green color table would have objects of many shades of green: blue-green, yellow-green, dark green, etc. The colors on the table could be changed from week to week to provide surprises.

Color Wheel That Spins. Color relationship can be demonstrated by a spinning color wheel. From cardboard cut a circle approximately 4 in. in diameter. Color it red, blue, and yellow. Begin with primary colors. Punch two small holes in the center of the circle as in a button. Thread the circle with twine about a yard long and tie the ends together. Roll the twine and then pull it. As you pull it, the twine winds and unwinds in a purring rhythm and turns the color chart at the same time. When two or more colors are side by side on a wheel, the colors blend in spinning. (Instructional Bulletin No. EC 4, Los Angeles City Schools.)

Flannel Board. Select a piece of heavy cardboard or plywood about 2 by 3 ft, depending upon the space available or the degree of portability desired. Cover this with outing flannel with fuzzy nap. Prepare pictures by pasting on the back of each picture small pieces of flannel, flocking paper with sensitized back, felt, or sandpaper. Press under heavy weight to avoid curling edges. Pictures adhere to flannel board.

A Pegboard. Use a pegboard and hooks. These are available at most hardware stores. Pupils select pictures that have rhyming names and hang them on the hooks. This lends itself to matching and rhyming pictures, names, and objects.

A "Breath" Game. Drop some small pieces of colored tissue

paper into a widemouthed jar, about 4 in. across and 4 or 5 in. high. A very slight breath across the open mouth of the jar will set the bits of paper to flying around like birds, and the children love to watch them and experiment with different volumes of breath. Anything that encourages a deaf child to use his breath with sustained effort is a good thing. (Suggested by Harriet Montague, "The Parents Talk It Over with Harriet Montague," *Volta Review*, 60:91, [Feb.] 1958).

Bubbles. Have fun blowing bubbles near the window or in the yard and watch the sunshine make rainbow colors in the bubbles.

Steps to Toyland. A game for young children from Parker Brothers, Inc., Salem, Massachusetts. The object of the game is to arrive in Toyland by moving from one colored step to another as directed by the color wheel spinner.

Balloon Man. 1. Playskool Puzzle No. 360–2. This Playskool wood inlaid puzzle plaque encourages concentration and relaxation.

2. Ben-G Push Out Puzzle. The push out colored balloons and color words may be used in teaching the names of colors. Children dramatize the Balloon Man. He sells balloons to children who ask for their balloons with a riddle, such as:

"May I have a balloon the color of an apple?"
"May I have a balloon the color of the grass?"
"May I have a balloon the color of grapes?"

Tic-Tac-Toe. Make a game board of cardboard or posterboard 9 by 9 in. square. Mark off in 3-in. squares. Have two envelopes, one for each player, in which are placed 2½-in. squares of colored paper. On the outside of each envelope paste a square denoting the color for that player. Play the same as Tic-Tac-Toe game with each player saying the color as he places the paper in a square.

Rainbow Colors. Make a rainbow lotto game by preparing a 9- by 9-in. cardboard. With India ink divide this into six sections as indicated. Cut colored paper disks or use colored plastic disks. Say these lines as the disks are placed in the sections on the board:

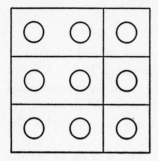

We mix rainbow colors.
Red and yellow make orange.
Yellow and blue make green.
Blue and red make purple.

Games to Play

"What Is Its Color?" Show the class a toy, a piece of paper, or a cloth of a certain color. Have one child run lightly around the room and touch one or more objects of the same color. The teacher makes certain that there are many colored objects in view in the room so that children may find them successfully.

"What Color Is Missing?" Make six balls of colored yarn, one for each primary and secondary color. Place the balls on a table while children study and observe them. Have children look the opposite direction while one child removes one ball of yarn, then asks the question, "What color is missing?"

Variations of this game:

Fill six large glass salt shakers with dry calcimine or tempera paint, one for each primary and secondary color. These may be used instead of the balls of colored yarn for above game.

They can later be used for finger painting by first placing a starch mixture on the paper, then sprinkling the colored paint from the shaker, and finally spreading with fingers and hands to make a picture.

"What Color Am I?" Make a set of riddle cards, each having a picture and a question. The following pictures and questions are suggestions:

I am an apple. What color am I?
I am carrots. What color am I?

I am a stop sign. What color am I?
I am a go sign. What color am I?

"Hide the Colored Thimble." Buy several colored thimbles at the ten cent store. Use these for playing the game, "Hide a Colored Thimble." Place a thimble in full view but in an unexpected place while one child hides his eyes or is out of the room. When he returns, direct his hunting by clapping loudly when he approaches the thimble and softly when he goes away from it.

Color Wheel (for younger children). Attach strips of colored crepe paper, about 4-ft lengths, to a band of heavy paper which will be worn around the waist of one child who will be the hub of the wheel. Other children hold the ends of the crepe paper strips and walk slowly around in a circle as they sing:

> "Here we go round the color wheel,
> The color wheel, the color wheel.
> Here we go round the color wheel,
> Early in the morning."
> (Sung to the tune of "The Mulberry Bush.")

Watching for a Rainbow. *Art Stories, Book One,* William Garrison Whitford, Edna B. Liek, and William Scott Gray (Scott, Foresman and Company, Chicago, 1933) offers many suggestions for learning about a rainbow and rainbow colors.

An effective paper rainbow can be made by tearing colored art paper and pasting the pieces together to form a rainbow for a poster or picture.

Song to be used with rainbow picture:

> "Red and orange, green and blue,
> Shining yellow, purple too,
> All the colors that I know
> Live up in the rainbow."
> (Sung to the tune of "Color."[2])

[2] From *New Games and Songs* by Ethel Croninshield. Boston Music Company, 1941, p. 5.

Make a large rainbow by using long streamers of colored crepe paper; one end of each is fastened to a piece of cardboard and secured to the wall, much higher than the children's heads. The loose end of each strip can be held by a child as colors are named and as the song is sung.

Color Wheel (for older children). A large color wheel made from three sizes of circles is used in teaching secondary colors. The larger circle is divided into six segments that are colored violet, blue, green, yellow, orange, and red. On the segments of the middle circle, which is placed on top of the large circle, the names of the colors are written in. The smaller circle, placed on the top of all, has arrows which indicate the secondary color made by two primary colors. Circles are held together with a roundhead paper fastener.

Each child is given a circle made from drawing paper which has been divided into six equal segments.

Aloud: "You have a circle that looks like this. [Hold up circle.] We are going to make a color wheel, and we are going to play a game while we are doing it. I am going to give you a sentence about a color but I will not use the name of the color. If you know what I am saying and can write the word in the correct place on the wheel, raise your hand. Then you may give the next sentence. Let's start this way. . . ."

Aloud: "The color I am thinking of is the color of grass."

Silent: The pupils repeat this sentence. The student who raises his hand first comes to the front and gives his answer. Then he gives a sentence from which the class can write another color. When the six colors have been guessed and written in the color wheel, the class may color their wheels.

The Merry Bell Game. This happy game makes use of colors and small bells which the players ring as they spin their color on the dial, and when it stops on a picture. (Milton Bradley Company, Springfield, Mass., 1957, Game # 4713.)

Clown Puzzle. A clown puzzle is dittoed so that each child has his own puzzle.

> *Aloud:* "Here is a picture of a clown. At the top of the paper are the color words. See if you can put each in its proper place. The first letter of each word is in the box to help you. Only one letter goes in each box. You may want to color the clown."

Books and Stories

The Color Kittens by Margaret Wise Brown (published by Simon and Schuster, Inc., New York, 1949) is a whimsical story about kittens who discover how to make new colors by mixing paints. Glass tumblers of water and paint are used for actually making the colors as the story is told.

Red Light, Green Light by Golden MacDonald and Leonard Weisgard (published by Doubleday & Company, Inc., New York, 1944) might be called "A Traffic Lesson for Tiny Tots," and is easily used as an outgrowth of the color unit. The record, "The Little Fat Policeman," supplements the story (R 45, a Golden Record distributed by Simon and Schuster, Inc., New York).

SECTION 4
FARM ANIMALS
by
Miriam Keslar

The following material has been planned for use with a unit of the farm. It provides many opportunities for recognizing farm animals and their names.

Presenting Pictures

Print the words, FARM ANIMALS, on the blackboard. Have pictures of the animals mounted on poster board. Have names of animals on cards.

Hold up a picture of each animal, one at a time, and describe each. Place the pictures against the blackboard and put the name of the animal in front of each.

CLOWN PUZZLE

blue	purple	black
yellow	green	brown
red	orange	

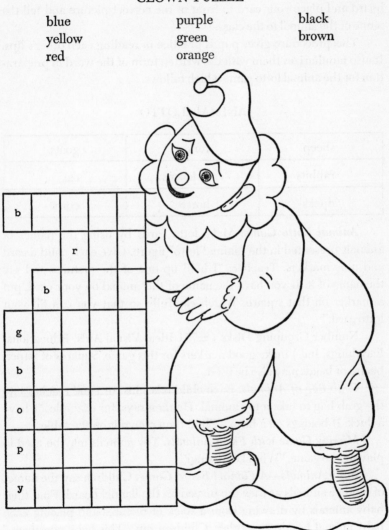

Next, take the cards from in front of the pictures and distribute them to the children in the class. Teacher: "Now we will play a game. As I say the name of the animal, you are to watch my lips to see if you have the card with the name of that animal. If you do, come up to the board and place your card in front of the correct picture and tell the name of the animal to the class."

This procedure gives pupils practice in reading each other's lips. It also familiarizes them with the written form of the word in preparation for the animal lotto game which follows.

ANIMAL LOTTO

sheep	turkey	goats
rabbits	chickens	cat
ducks	horse	cows

Animal Lotto Game. Make lotto cards by using the names of animals presented in the "animal lotto" figure. Give each child a card and nine markers. Teacher: "I hold up one of the pictures and say the name of it. If you have the name of this animal on your card, put a marker on that square. Watch carefully so that you can fill your lotto card."

Number Grouping Disks (#751 Ideal Visual Aids, Educational Playthings, Inc.) make good markers for this game. Squares of paper, beans, or beads may also be used.

Grab Bag of Animals. Each child takes his turn and reaches into the grab bag to take a toy animal. He then says, for example, "I have a duck. It belongs on a farm." Child then places it on the table.

Missing Game with Farm Animals. Toy animals may be used in playing the game, "What Is Missing?"

Baby Animals—A Flannel Board Game. Children say the names of mother animals as they are placed on the flannel board. Find their baby animals by drawing from a stack of pictures and placing each baby animal beside its mother. Children say, "This baby goes here."

Baby Animals (*a Game for Independent Work*). Pictures of animals are pasted on an 11- by 14-in. poster board as indicated. A string is secured at the back by knotting and bringing it through the cardboard, one string at the right of each picture of the mother animals. A roundhead paper fastener is placed at the left of each picture of a baby animal. The game is played by looping each string around a fastener, thus connecting pictures of animals that belong together. (Pictures used were cut from the reading readiness book, *Here We Go*, by Emmett A. Betts and Mabel O'Donnell; Row, Peterson & Company, Evanston, Ill., 1954 edition.)

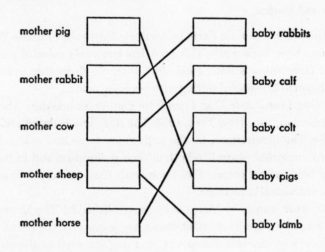

Educational Games (Bibliography)

On the Farm Lotto. Ed-u-Cards, Inc., New York. Pictures include farm animals, pets, flowers, fruits, vegetables, and tools.

A B C Lotto. Ed-U-Cards, Inc., New York. A lotto game with objects and numbers.

Go-Together Lotto. Ed-U-Cards, Inc., New York, 1956. Includes pictures of objects that go together. Encourages observation.

Farmyard Puzzle. Advanced Farmyard Puzzle, Sifo Toys, No. 1 K.

Missing Faces Puzzle. An Educator Ben–G Puzzle, No. 1. Reading fun with matching words and faces. Includes faces of animals and people.

Puppets

Hand puppets are made from fruits or vegetables, spools, wooden blocks, stuffed socks, or paper sacks. The latter are good for animal puppet faces.

Stick puppets are made from heavy paper or cardboard, toy animals or dolls.

Books and Stories

The Animals of Friendly Farm by Marjorie Hartwell; Franklin Watts, Inc., New York, 1946. This book has large and colorful pictures of farm animals with good story lines. Each mother animal is shown in a beautiful setting with her baby animal.

Little Dog Lost, Little Dog Found, by Esphyr Slobodkins; Abelard-Schuman, Inc., New York, 1956. The story line is direct and simple. The illustrations, by the author, are large and colorful and are somewhat posterlike both in their delineation and in the use of bold, bright colors. This book lends itself to story telling and to individual enjoyment.

Ask Mr. Bear, a story by Marjorie Flack, published by The Macmillan Company, New York, 1932. Paper bag puppets of the horse, cow, duck, pig, chicken, sheep, cat, and dog are used as the story is dramatized.

Paddy—the Fuzzy Wuzzy Duckling, by Nettie Weber; Whitman Publishing Company, Racine, Wis., 1949. A story about a little lost duck who tries to find his mother. Pictures are large and colorful. The pictures and story make a very interesting flannel-board story.

The Woolly Lamb, by Helen Hoke and Natalie Fox. Illustrated by Julian Messner, Inc., New York, 1942. A story of a little lost lamb who tries to find his mother. A fuzzy picture book. Good for a flannel-board story.

Story of the Little Cowboy, by Arleen Caster. A build-up flannel-
board story. Makes a very good exercise for speechreading when
picture parts are removed from the board. Also makes a good
story for two children to play together. Story unpublished—
available from the Speech Correction Office, Los Angeles City
Schools.

Presentation of Materials, Lessons, and Stories

In the presentation of materials, lessons, and stories the teacher
strives for ease, naturalness, fluency, poise, and animation. All these
are essential to masterful presentation. It is a goal worth striving for
and, when acquired, adds immeasurably to the pleasure as well as to
the value of the work.

SECTION 5

WHERE DOES THE RAIN COME FROM?

Mrs. Ethel Drake skillfully uses the Socratic method in her
dramatization of "Where the Rain Comes From." She builds her concepts of condensation and evaporation from a concrete experiment
using the formation of steam from a boiling teakettle. She makes a
difficult lesson in science meaningful and vivid for her pupils by leading them from their familiar experience to the concepts on the abstract
level.

"A Dramatization"
by
Ethel L. Drake[1]

"The mist and cloud will turn to rain,
The rain to mist and cloud again."

H. W. Longfellow

[1] Ethel L. Drake, M.A., is a teacher of the deaf in the daytime classes of the
public schools in Alhambra, California. Some of her pupils attend the regular
classes part time.

(Interior of classroom. Table, blackboard, kettle, electric stove, table model. Pitcher of water, bowl of ice, flat pan, terrarium, long-handled mirror, umbrella. Teacher greets children as they hang up raincoats, take off galoshes, set umbrellas to dry. Some children take their seats. A few stand at the window. View of sky from window.)

Tom:	(*At window.*) It's stopped raining.
Bill:	Look at the big, dark clouds.
Teacher:	I think it will rain again, very soon. Those are rain clouds.
Bill:	What makes the rain, Miss Parks?
Sandy:	(*Comes close to teacher.*) Where does the rain come from? What makes the rain?
Tom:	The rain comes from the sky.
Sandy:	From the sky?
Bill:	(*Pointing.*) From the clouds.
Sandy:	How does the water get way up there? What keeps the water in the clouds?
Timmie:	What makes the clouds, Miss Parks?
Teacher:	I thought you'd want to talk about rain, boys and girls. Look what I have here. (*Points to table standing in front of blackboard. Takes paper cover off top of long table. On table is small electric stove. Kettle on stove. Other props on table.*)
	(*Timmie starts to touch kettle.*)
	Don't touch the kettle. It has hot water in it. I'm going to turn up the heat and make the water so hot that it will boil. (*Turns up heat.*)
	Now watch the spout. This is called the spout. (*Points.*) I'll write the word. Let's all say it—spout.

Children:	Spout.
Teacher:	What do you see, Tom? (*Points to steam issuing from spout.*)
Tom:	It's a cloud.
Sandy:	It looks like a little cloud.
Timmie:	Does the water make that? How?
Teacher:	The water got warm. We made it change. This little cloud of water . . . . (*Points to steam.*)
Sandy:	It's not water. (*Shaking her head.*)
Teacher:	Yes, there is water there. I'll show you. (*Takes up long-handled mirror. Holds mirror near to the steam issuing from kettle's spout.*) What do you see?
Sandy:	The glass got wet. How? Where did the water come from? (*Draws her finger over glass.*)
Teacher:	You can't see the water, but it is in the air. First the hot water came out of the spout as a gas. We call it water vapor. (*Writes word on board spelled and phonetically with diacritical marks.*) Here (*points to space just beyond spout*) the gas comes out. When it reaches the air it changes to steam. We can see the steam. That's all water.
Bill:	Is that little cloud filled with water?
Tom:	Why can't we see the water?
Teacher:	You can't see the water because it is made up of little drops—not drops like this . . . (*takes spoonful of water and makes a drop fall to the table*) but very, very small drops of water. So small you can't see them. They are tiny drops. (*Writes tiny on board as above.*)

Timmie:	(*Points to kettle.*) Is all the water gone?
Teacher:	No, not all. But some of the water went up into the air. We say it evaporated. Let's write that word on the board and learn to say it. (*Writes as above.*)
Children:	(*As teacher claps out syllable rhythm.*) E-vap-o-rat-ed!
Teacher:	Again! (*Children repeat word.*)
Timmie:	(*Moving hand in air.*) I can't see the water in the air.
Sandy:	And I can't feel it.
Teacher:	Now, let's heat a little water in this pan. (*Puts a small amount of water into flat pan. Turns heat high.*)
Timmie:	Look, the water is moving around. (*Water boils.*)
Tom:	It's . . . (*hesitates*) it's bubbling.
Teacher:	That's right, Tom. The water is bubbling. When water gets very hot, it bubbles.
Timmie:	The water is all gone! (*Points to pan.*)
Sandy:	(*Takes pan up by handle. Turns it upside down.*)
Teacher:	Tell me, Sandy, where is the water?
Sandy:	In the air.
Teacher:	How did it get there? Tom, let's use our new word.
Tom:	The water (*short pause as he looks at blackboard*) evaporated.
Timmie:	Will it come down in our room, again?
Teacher:	No, there is not enough water in the air, here. (*Points to the window.*) But there, outside, there is a lot of water in the air. Our little bit of water will fly out and make friends with the other drops of water.
Sandy:	How does the water outside get warm so that it can go up in the air?

Tom:	Who heats the water in the ocean? The water can't evaporate when it's cold.
Teacher:	Let's look at our terrarium. (*Teacher and children go to chest. Terrarium stands on chest before window.*) See the little pan of water there. Now let's open the lid of our glass box. Put your hand in here, Tom. Is the air warm or cold?
Tom:	It's warm.
Teacher:	Is the air dry or does it feel a little bit wet?
Tom:	It's . . . .
Teacher:	We say the air is damp. Not wet, not dry, but damp. Why is the air so warm in our terrarium?
Bill:	I know. Yesterday we had a sunny day. The sun warmed the glass and the water got warm, too.
Teacher:	Yes, that is true. The water held the heat of the sun and helped to keep the inside of the terrarium warm.
Timmie:	(*Points to side of glass.*) Look, it's raining on the glass.
Teacher:	Let's feel the outside of the glass, now. Is it warm or cool?
Sandy:	The glass is cold.
Teacher:	The cold air from outside makes the tiny drops of water in the air—inside—come together, and we see the drops of water on the glass.
	There is another word to tell about this. We say the water in the air condenses. We'll put that word on the board, too. (*Writes word on board as before.*) Let's all say it together.
Children:	Con-den-ses.
Teacher:	So now we know that when water goes up into the air and we can't see it—we say the water evaporates.

When we can see the water again, we say the water in the air is condensed—or the water condenses.

Let's try something else. (*Shows pitcher of water and and bowl of ice.*) The water is cold, but I'll make it colder. I'll put ice in it to make the water very cold.

Now we'll turn on the gas again to make our kettle steam. There, it didn't take long because the water was hot. We'll put the pitcher of cold water near the hot steam. . . . What do you see, Bill?

Bill: (*Touches outside of pitcher.*) It's wet. There is water on the pitcher. On the outside!

Teacher: Who can tell me what happened?

Sandy: The water in the steam touched the cold pitcher and . . . .

Teacher: (*Points to word on board.*) The water in the steam cloud condensed.

Sandy: (*Repeats word.*) Condensed. It condensed.

Teacher: Who can tell me where the rain comes from? Think, now!

Bill: The sun makes the water warm. . . .

Timmie: Where's the water?

Bill: There's water in the ground . . . and water in the ocean . . . and water in the rivers. . . .

Teacher: That's right, Bill. There is water all over our earth. Go on, Bill.

Bill: Well, the sun makes the water warm. The sun changes the water and it goes up into the sky, and makes clouds in the sky.

Teacher: What does the water do? Use the right word?

Bill:	The water (*looks at the board*) evaporates.
Timmie:	Well . . . the sun makes the water go up into the air, but what makes it come down?
Sandy:	Oh, Timmie, don't you remember? The clouds are all stuffed with water, like a . . . a . . . pillow. Maybe the air gets colder. . . .
Timmie:	Then what happens?
Sandy:	The rain comes down!
Timmie:	It rains? (*Doubtfully.*) Well. . . .
Teacher:	Timmie, do you remember the water on the glass sides of the terrarium? Let's all look at it again.
	The air is hot inside. But the air outside is not as hot. The cold air makes the water in the air inside. . . .
Tom: *Bill:* *Sandy:*	CONDENSE!
Timmie:	And it rains. (*Said as if he had discovered it himself.*)
Teacher:	Let's take our seats now. Sandy, bring in my umbrella. (*Sandy goes to hall and brings in teacher's umbrella.*) When I came to school, early this morning, my umbrella was wet. It's not wet now. It's dry. Timmie, where did the water go?
Timmie:	The water . . . (*hesitates*). . . .
Tom:	Remember, Timmie, the water. . . .
Timmie:	(*Almost shouting.*) Evaporated! It went up into the air.
	Look, it's raining again! (*Points to the window.*) The water from your umbrella helped to make more rain. (*Children all crowd to window.*)

End

Bibliography

Schneider, H. and N. Schneider. *Science for Here and Now*. D. C. Heath and Company, Boston, 1959.

Thorn, Sam, and Irene Harbeck. *Let's Find Out*, Beckley-Cardy Company, Chicago, 1951.

PART VI

THE HEARING-IMPAIRED CHILD
IN "INTEGRATED" CLASSES

"INTEGRATED" CLASSES
IN CALIFORNIA

Recent developments in medicine, electronics, and child psychology have given a new impetus to the habilitation of hearing-impaired children. A primary goal of the education of hearing-impaired children is constant exposure to a friendly and stimulating oral environment. This, it is believed, can awaken the child's interest and can develop his ability to interpret living and learning situations. Guided by a specially trained teacher,[1] a hearing-impaired child is made ready to join the regular classes with hearing children and to develop the habit of associating and studying with them.

In California, the integration of hearing-impaired children with their hearing contemporaries in regular schools was made possible when, in 1943, the State Department of Public Health and Education provided an appropriation for the expansion of a program of hearing conservation and of education for hearing-impaired children. Educational authorities of the Compton Public Schools in 1948 established special day classes for the deaf and hard-of-hearing children to prepare them to be placed in regular classes with hearing children.

The basic philosophy underlying this decision to integrate hearing and nonhearing children in the public schools was as follows:[2]

[1] Special classes for the hearing-impaired in which the children are given instruction in speechreading, auditory training, and speech for part of the day. The rest of the time is spent attending classes with the normal hearing children.
[2] From a report of Halldora K. Sigurdson at the Claremont College Reading Conference, 16th Yearbook Claremont Colleges, Claremont, California, 1948.

1. Modern developments in acoustics, electronics and educational methods point to the possibility of integrating educationally an increasing number of hearing-handicapped children.

2. The hearing-handicapped children might have much to gain in the way of emotional enrichment, desirable behavior patterns, and motivation for verbal communication by close and continuous association with hearing children.

3. In an integrated school situation it is possible to use special equipment, personnel, and methodology needed for effective specialized work with hearing-impaired children.

4. Since deaf and hard-of-hearing children live in the world of persons who hear and speak, it would be advantageous if their adjustment to such an environment commenced as early as possible during their impressionable learning years.

5. Nonhandicapped children can also profit from association with those not so fortunate. This "integrated" arrangement is mutually beneficial to both groups.

SECTION 2

THE PROCESS OF INTEGRATION[1]
(As Seen by a Special Teacher of Hearing-impaired Children)
by
Rose Pissakov[2]

The concept of integration is used with flexibility. Each child's readiness for integration is judged on an individual basis with the consideration of psychological, language, and academic factors. Children "grow" into integration. They are given many opportunities to observe and share experiences with hearing children.

[1] Some educational procedures which are intended to prepare the hearing-impaired child to enter regular classes with hearing children are given in Part III, Section 3; Part IV, Sections 2 and 5; and Part V, Sections 3 and 5.

[2] Alhambra Public Schools.

1. They are on the playground together.
2. They are in the cafeteria together.
3. They participate in the physical education periods together.
4. They go on field trips together.
5. They go into hearing classes in those areas of learning in which they can participate successfully and profitably.

The hearing children from regular classes have an opportunity to visit the special classes. They are given to understand how people learn to talk, why hearing-impaired children talk as they do, and how they can all be helped. They are shown how to read the lips and how to use hearing aids. They themselves listen through hearing aids. Mutual understanding between the two groups is developed, and the life of the hearing-impaired child is enriched.

Section 3

THE PROCESS OF INTEGRATION OF HEARING-IMPAIRED CHILDREN
(As Seen by a Teacher of Regular Classes)
by
Nancy Blue[1]

A hearing-impaired child who is integrated in a hearing classroom is made at once to feel that he is a part of the group. Hearing children in the regular classes become accustomed to hearing-impaired children and have techniques of their own in talking to them. The hearing-impaired child participates most readily in such subjects as social studies, arithmetic, spelling, and writing. Reading is more difficult because of his limited vocabulary.

In social studies, the hearing-impaired child has the opportunity

[1] Granada School, Alhambra, California.

to work with hearing children and to cooperate with the group. Arithmetic, spelling, and writing are subjects which can be learned from blackboard work or with individual help.

It is necessary for the classroom teacher to know that placing the hearing-impaired child in the front of the room is very important. If he is in the front of the room, it is easier to get the child's attention and to give him directions which he can understand. The light should fall properly upon the teacher's face. The classroom teacher who has hearing-impaired children in her class unconsciously finds herself speaking more slowly, enunciating more clearly, and facing the group. She is more alert when giving individual instructions and showing the place in the book where the lesson assignment is. Without neglecting her own group, she makes sure that the hearing-impaired child has understood the assignment.

The amazing part of the integration program is how much the hearing child helps the one who is hearing-impaired. Children learn how to communicate with each other by means of language and natural gestures. When the teacher cannot get ideas across, sometimes the hearing child can convey the message for her.

Integration is important because both groups learn that they can communicate with each other under the normal conditions of the classroom. Thus, the hearing-impaired child is enabled to lead a richer and fuller life and his personality parallels that of a child with no physical handicap.

Some Cases

Randy had a hearing impairment.[2] For the first four months, Randy was not integrated because he was so very shy and withdrawn. Gradually, he began to play with other children on the playground. During this period, he became friends with a few of the hearing children.

By the end of the semester, Randy was ready to come into the classroom for all the subjects except social studies. He was able to

[2] Congenital, moderately deaf.

take part in all third-grade academic work. He then spent the afternoons with his special teacher.

Randy read with the second-grade group. He participated in this group in oral reading, answering and asking questions, and taking part in the discussions. The rest of his work was done with the third graders. He became completely a part of the group, as was shown by this excerpt from his record:

1. Asking other children for help.
2. Helping others with their work.
3. Playing activity games with a partner.
4. At times, being reminded he was talking too much.
5. Singing with the group.
6. Doing group work.

Joan and Christine[3] came in for half an hour of arithmetic and spelling. They had little speech or hearing, but both tried very hard. They talked to the other children, asking questions, commenting on haircuts or dresses, and noticing new things in the room. Some of this communication was done by gestures or actual pointing. Their work was always completed, their homework was always done, and their actual classwork was very good. Both of these girls were older than Randy and felt differently toward integration. They felt very important at being allowed to work in a regular classroom.

It is hard to describe specifically, step by step, how these children actually were integrated into the regular classroom. They fitted into the program and, with some few exceptions, they received the same treatment as did their hearing classmates.

[3] Both girls are congenitally and profoundly deaf.

SECTION 4

ORAL ENVIRONMENT IN AN "INTEGRATED" SCHOOL
by
Myra Jane Taylor and Carleda Moore[1]

Each school for hearing-impaired children[2] has in its basic curriculum guide some statement that one of the objectives of the school or department is to prepare children for life. Some of these statements place greater emphasis on lifelike situations than do others.

The "preparation for life" of a hearing-impaired child means the development of his potential abilities so that he can apply them successfully in coping with situations he encounters in the hearing world. This preparation must be started early in the child's life. He has to develop the habit of feeling he is a part of the hearing group, of learning the rules of the game, and of acquiring a strong motivation to make himself understood by others, as well as a desire to understand them. Only in an atmosphere of daily contact with hearing children in school can he develop attitudes and habits of oral communication.

Every opportunity is utilized by teachers of regular classes and by the specially trained teachers of the deaf in day classes to arrange for these contacts with the hearing children in the classroom, on the playground, in the cafeteria, and at social events. The special teacher of day classes emphasized language work in preparation for the child's participation in regular classes with hearing children. The hearing-impaired child learns at firsthand, through direct observation and participation, the "integrative" behavior patterns of hearing children.

[1] Myra Jane Taylor, M.A., supervisor of aural education and speech, Compton City School District, Compton, California. Carleda Moore, A.B., coordinator of aural education, Compton Union Secondary School District, Compton, California, and mother of a junior-high-school-age deaf girl.

[2] The majority of those classed as "hearing-impaired children" in the Compton Public Schools are severely and profoundly deaf, or moderately and severely hard of hearing.

Participating in youth group activities in each child's own neighborhood is considered an avenue to learning in life situations. A certain unit of the Camp Fire Girls organization has received a national award for its cooperation with an integrated-school-program's parent group and its faculty. Any girl of seven or more is granted camping privileges, whether a Camp Fire member or not. During the last five years, 5 to 10 deaf and hard-of-hearing girls have participated each year. The older girls, now in junior high school, are given added responsibilities as they demonstrate their ability to assume them.

Care is taken that these girls do not become a unit apart from the others. These girls are housed according to age group in the camp, taking turns in the routine which makes use of verbal communication. Hearing participants learn to keep trying to understand by frankly admitting, "I do not understand. Who or what are you talking about?" The desirability for more accurate speech prompts each deaf and hard-of-hearing girl to take more care in enunciation.

These young girls hold offices as do hearing members of the group. When one such profoundly deaf child was chosen president of the camp group, she understood her duties and functioned so well that she was re-elected by popular demand.

Scout groups—boys and girls—take the same interest and plan in cooperation with the parents and teachers. They find these children bring real contributions to the group.

Track-meet time in the elementary division is exciting. The deaf and hard-of-hearing child really holds his own. Last year, a certain sixth-grade boy competed in the baseball throw for distance. It was great fun to watch this *profoundly* deaf boy taking in all the instruction from his hearing classmates and regular classroom teacher. When the final day arrived, he was coached and encouraged by his classmates.

The teachers (hearing class and special class) commented as they listened. Far across the field were shouted all the appropriate words of a sports event. "Let 'er go!" "Come on fellow!"

On the last throw his opponent, a hearing boy of another class, outdistanced his best throw by one-quarter of an inch.

What a disappointment!

Not for him. His classmates told him how good he was, how many points he had earned. They insisted the other fellow's throw was a lucky one.

No isolation here. A warmth of feeling that you are important because you are you. There was a similar appreciation for the academic excellence of this deaf boy. It was commented upon by the hearing on many occasions.

When the hearing and nonhearing grow up together, there is mutual respect based upon an understanding of each other as is found in all real-life situations. This is evidenced by the committee work on projects in the regular classroom. A profoundly deaf girl was *chairman of the committee* whose project was making a mural of South America. Her talent as an artist was recognized, and she had to plan with the children how and what was to be accomplished.

Several deaf and hard-of-hearing students were enrolled last year in the school orchestra. Two severely hard-of-hearing students played wind instruments, and a profoundly deaf boy played in the percussion section on the big bass drum or cymbals. One year, a profoundly deaf student of the department played the drums in the all-city orchestra of 130 members representing 20 schools.

Integration of the hard-of-hearing and deaf students on the junior- and senior-high-school level with hearing students is a reality in some areas. By the time these students have finished elementary school, they should be ready and willing to face many new life situations and feel competent that they can do a good job commensurate with their abilities. Some students have more of the characteristics that lend themselves to being successful in an integrated-school situation than do others. Many of the students in the secondary aural education program are accepting and facing new situations that make them feel confident and successful.

Parents of these students have a great deal to do with the adjustment and success made by their sons or daughters in the hearing world. Is the parent willing to go out of his way to be sure his child is being placed in life situations? Is the parent understanding his child's

special problems? Is the parent willing to plan and serve on commit-
tees for community needs and resources? Is the parent really interested in his aurally handicapped child?

One of the activities that has proven beneficial and has certainly
added color and acceptance to the deaf and hard-of-hearing students'
social life has been their participation in a dancing group of around
fifty teen-age boys and girls. This dance program is a well planned
and coordinated activity in which parents are asked to assist by greet-
ing the teen-agers and helping to serve refreshments. Manners and
the social graces are taught along with dance techniques.

Two of the profoundly deaf students out of six in the eighth-grade
class made honor scholarship in competition with the hearing students. This meant they had to make A's or B's in their subjects of
science, history, mathematics, English, physical education, and one
elective. Cooperation between special and regular classroom teachers
prepared and made it possible for these two students to excel in their
subjects.

Vocabulary of the course context is gone over by the special
teacher, and the student is prepared for further study. Tests and daily
assignments are the same for hearing and nonhearing students. Hearing pals often study with their deaf friends.

Some of the students have entered competitive sports and have
gained both success and recognition. A profoundly deaf girl student
was chosen as tennis partner with a hearing classmate to represent a
school of over 1,000 pupils in the Southern California Tournament at
Pasadena last year.

We know and realize that some aurally impaired students will do
a better job of integrating than others; just as with the hearing students, some are shy and reserved and others are gregarious and out-
going. We feel that we must give these students every opportunity
for learning to live in a hearing world by putting them into life situations.

PART VII

INTENSIVE TRAINING IN SPEECHREADING WITH LIFE-SITUATION FILMS

SECTION 1

LIFE-SITUATION FILMS
AND ORAL COMMUNICATION

Use of Films for Training

As a hearing-impaired child grows and advances in school, he needs to receive more complicated verbal instruction and to learn to express himself orally. For intensive training in speechreading and oral communication, life-situation films are used to advantage as an oral-language aid.

Each film contains an episode which is acted out on the screen with a background of settings and action. The child sees the close-ups of the speakers and their moving lips as they speak. The speech sounds are amplified by means of a group hearing aid. The child's speech perception is strengthened by using special exercises and adding kinesthetic-rhythmic and tactile sensory data. Allowed to view the film several times, the child learns to notice more and more details of the spoken words without losing sight of the meaning of situations as wholes. The repeated showings of the same film do not become monotonous to the child, for with each showing he is given a new assignment. Gradually, he learns to unravel words and sentences in new settings and acquires spontaneity in speechreading. The teacher follows the child's progress from film to film by counting the number of words the child speechreads correctly. The child himself is encouraged by seeing his improvement in understanding speech.

Fluent and accurate speechreading requires the development of various abilities. The two most important ones are (1) ability to retain the continuity of spoken words, and (2) synthetic-analytic ability.

Continuity of Spoken Words

Life-situation films serve as a sort of "book of spoken words." By seeing these films repeatedly, the hearing-impaired child gradually absorbs a continuity of spoken words, in contrast to the hearing child who acquires this continuity spontaneously by hearing speech continuously. The hearing-impaired child, by retaining this continuity of words in his memory, is able to fill in the gaps of the words he misses in speechreading and to anticipate the words of the speaker. As he advances in his reading and writing ability, he learns to differentiate the continuity of printed and written words in contrast to the way they are seen on the lips and heard in oral language.

Synthetic-analytic Ability

A synthetic-analytic ability is fundamental in speechreading. As the name implies, the analysis of speech in the learning situation must not become divorced from the child's perceptions of word meanings. With this ability, the child can understand speech by putting together various details he observes. These details are revealed while working with the film such as:

1. The visible background of the picture, gestures, facial expressions, and handling of objects by film characters.
2. Patterns of words seen on the lips, already familiar to the child.
3. Key words that help to convey the meaning of the sentence.
4. Fragments and/or vibrations of speech sounds recognized through amplification.
5. Kinesthetic and tactile awareness of the movements of speech.
6. Interpretation of the meaning from the verbal context of words and from the grammatical-syntactic structure of sentences.
7. The rhythm of stressed and unstressed parts of words, of emphasis in sentences, of pauses, and of intonation of the voice.
8. Clues which are conveyed by the teacher's explanation, spoken or written on the blackboard.

The child's synthetic-analytic ability is put into practice by dramatizing the film story and by conversing about details related to the theme of the story.

The Teacher's Preparation

Life-situation films are to be used as aids to oral language and are not to be used mechanically. They are a tool for creative teaching. In order to understand the principles of the "life-situation" approach, the teacher must study the script of the film and plan her lessons so that she can use this approach creatively.

In order to relate the story of the film to the child's own experience and interest, the teacher asks him questions before he has seen the film the first time. In later showings of the film, the teacher is able to direct the child's attention to parts of the story and to specific words which he did not understand. With a variety of exercises, she clarifies the difficult words and expressions and makes the precise meaning of the details of the story stand out. A competent teacher succeeds in making the child want to improve his speechreading and speech.

SECTION 2

TOMMY'S TABLE MANNERS[1]
Film Script No. 1[2]

Cast: Mother, Father, Tommy, Fred.

Father:	Did you wash your hands, Tommy?
Tommy:	Yes.
Father:	Well, you missed some of the dirt, Tommy. You'd better go and try again.

[1] Two series of life-situation films were produced by the Cinema Department of the University of Southern California. This film is the first of the second series (color and sound).

[2] Mrs. Rose Pissakov and Mrs. Cristine Jennings also contributed to the writing of the dialogues in the films, "Tommy's Table Manners," "Magic," "Barbara's New Shoes."

Fred:	(*Strange noises.*)
Father:	Fred, we don't make noises at the table.
Fred:	Can't I even talk?
Father:	Yes, of course you can talk, but we don't make those funny noises at the table.
Mother:	Father, will you come in and help me, please?
Father:	Of course.
Fred:	Did you get your face clean?
Tommy:	Yes. (*Reaches for the jelly.*) Where's Daddy?
Fred:	He's in the kitchen helping Mother. Don't stand up in your chair.
Tommy:	I can if I want to.
Fred:	Tommy, sit down, sit down!
Tommy:	I won't sit down.
Fred:	It's bad manners to stand in your chair. I'll tell Father. Father, come and see what Tommy's doing.
Father:	Why, Tommy. What are you doing? We don't stand up in our chairs.
Tommy:	I'm hungry.
Father:	I know, Tommy. We are all hungry, but polite people wait until everyone is at the table. Let's wait for Mother.
Tommy:	Daddy, what are table manners?
Father:	Well, Tommy, table manners are how we act at the table. A nice boy has good table manners.
Tommy:	Father, am I a nice boy?
Father:	Yes, Tommy, you're a nice boy. But sometimes you're not polite. Fred, Tommy needs help. Why don't you tell him about table manners?

Fred:	Well, one thing, Tommy, is that you don't put your elbows on the table. And you do not eat until everyone has come to the table.
Father:	And we sit quietly at the table.
Fred:	Yes.
Father:	Those are good table manners. How did you know them?
Fred:	Mother told me, and we learn table manners at school, too.
Father:	Yes, that's one of the ways we learn things. People have to tell us.
Tommy:	Did your mother tell you?
Father:	Yes, Tommy. My mother and father told me many things.
Tommy:	Were you a nice boy, Daddy?
Father:	I tried to be a nice boy, Tommy. But sometimes I forgot like Fred forgets.
Mother:	Thank you.
Tommy:	You see, Mommy, we waited for you.
Mother:	Thank you, Tommy, that is very nice.
Father:	No, Tommy, wait. We don't reach so far across the table.
Tommy:	Mommy, I'm hungry.
Mother:	Yes, I know you're hungry. But, Tommy, when food is far away on the table, you ask someone to pass it to you. You say, "Father, please pass the bread."
Tommy:	What do I say?
Mother:	You say, "Father, please pass the bread."
Tommy:	Father, ple . . . please . . . please. . . .

Mother:	Please pass. . . .
Tommy:	Father, please pass the bread. Father, I'm hungry. Please pass the bread.
Mother:	But we're not ready to eat yet. We always say a prayer before we eat, don't we? Wouldn't you like to say it for us?
Tommy:	Thank God for this food, and bless Daddy and Mommy, too, and please, God, make me a good boy.
Father:	Thank you, Tommy, that was very nice.
Tommy:	Father, please pass the bread.

Section 3

EXERCISES FOR INSTRUCTIONAL USE OF THE FILM, "TOMMY'S TABLE MANNERS"
by
Teachers of the California Public Schools[1]

Resourceful teachers will find many ways of making effective use of life-situation films. As suggestions for utilizing these films to advantage, five different instructional aspects of the films are identified: (1) the child's readiness, (2) the nonlanguage context of the film, (3) its language context, (4) the coordination of other sensory cues,[2] and (5) related topics. These five aspects are considered as they apply to each of the film scripts herein described.

[1] Mrs. Terry Chism, Mrs. Helen Dyer, Mr. Clark Harada, Mrs. Cristine Jennings, Mrs. Rose Pissakov, Mrs. Esther Rodgers, Miss Evelyn Shellgrain, Mrs. Mary Ann Strakosch, and Mrs. Irene Wassell.

[2] The teachers use these terms: (1) *cue* as hint, intimation, and (2) *clue* as thread for a guide (*cf.* Webster).

Readiness

Before showing the film, the following preparatory steps ensure the children's readiness to listen receptively and with purpose.

Speechreading Readiness. The teacher makes the students ready for the film which they are about to see by connecting the story situation with their life experiences. She establishes rapport with her students by asking questions about table manners they already know. This tie-up with the child's own past experiences is a key step in building readiness.

Questions

"How should we act when we are at the table?"

"Do *you* know someone who has good table manners?"

"Why do we have table manners?"

"How are your table manners at home? At school? On the playground?"

The teacher tells the story of the film very briefly, using some words or phrases from the dialogue of the film. The film is then shown.

Nonlanguage Context

After showing the film, the teacher asks questions to find out what nonverbal clues the students saw which helped them to understand the meaning of the story. Nonverbal clues may consist of actions, facial expressions, objects, and gestures.

Questions	Seen on Screen
"How many people are in the picture?"	Four.
"What are their names?"	Father, Mother, Fred, Tommy.
"What did Tommy forget to wash?"	His hands.
"What kind of noise did Fred make?"	Like an airplane.
"Who told Tommy to sit down in his chair?"	Fred.

"What did Mother bring in from the kitchen?"   Potatoes.

"What did Tommy start to eat when Father
went to the kitchen?"   The jelly.

"What did Tommy want Father to pass him?"   The bread.

Language Context

The teacher asks questions of the students to help them understand the key words, phrases, and sentences that reveal the meaning
of the story:

What did Father mean when he said,
"You *missed* some of the dirt?"   "Wash again."

Father said, "We don't make those
funny noises at the table." Why did
Father say that?   "Bad table manners."

Fred said, "It's bad manners to stand
in your chair." What do we mean by   (*Dramatize, using*
bad manners at the table? What do we   *definite contrast.*)
mean by *good manners* at the table?

Tommy said, "I'm hungry." He was im-   "Because polite
patient. Father answered, "Let's wait   people wait until
for Mother."   all are at the table."

(*Discuss the meaning of polite. Dramatize it, showing how it would look not
to wait for each other at the table.*)

Who said, "We don't reach so far   "Because we knock
across the table?" Why don't we reach   things over and it
across the table?   doesn't look nice."

(*Dramatize a situation of reaching
across the table. What do we do instead of reaching across the table? We
say, "Please pass the. . . ."*)

Who said, "We always say a *prayer* before we eat?" What does prayer mean? What other word means prayer? What does "Bless Daddy and Mommy" mean? What does "Make me a good boy" mean?

"Grace."

"Take care of."

"Help me to remember to be good to people."

(*Dramatize by using a prayer before nutrition time at school.*)

The film is again shown, for practice with familiar expressions and words that "go together." Expressions from the film dialogue are given, and new ones added.

"You missed some of the dirt."

> You missed some of your toys.
> You missed the train, the bus, the streetcar.
> You didn't wash off all the dirt.

"Get your face clean."

> Get your hands clean.
> Get your shoes clean.

"Wait for Mother."

> Wait for me.
> Wait for dinner.
> Wait for bedtime.
> Wait until morning.
> Wait until we get home.

"How did we act at the table?" ("How did we behave?")

> How did we act at school?
> How did we act on the bus?

The Coordination of Other Sensory Cues

The film is shown again, this time for more accurate meaning. The teacher gives exercises in sensory training and discrimination of word details in connection with the film situation, coordinating the students' auditory, visual, kinesthetic-rhythmic, and tactile senses. The following materials are adapted to the ability-level of the students.

Other Sensory Enrichment. Various adaptations are made of the context with the use of hearing aids:

1. Choric speech in which teacher and students speak a rhyme or jingle together.

Ready to Eat	*Wash Your Face*
I washed my hands.	Wash your hands!
I washed my face.	Wash your face!
I combed my hair.	What will I get?
Now may I say grace?	With a nice clean face?
	(*Children make wishes.*)

2. Expressions for rhythm.

Sit down.	Wait for me.
I'm hungry.	Wait a minute.
Thank you.	I forgot.
Please wait.	What do I say?

3. By seeing and feeling (kinesthetic-rhythmic training) with reduced voice. The teacher takes familiar expressions from the dialogue and any other related expressions and claps out the rhythm, repeating the words at the same time. Then she claps these phrases without saying the words, and students guess the correct expressions.

I'm hungry.	Don't stand in your chair.
I'm hungry as a bear.	Please pass the bread.
Sit quietly at the table.	Don't make so much noise.

4. By hearing (auditory training) with hearing aids and without seeing lips. The teacher gives discrimination words to students who write words as they hear them without seeing the teacher's lips. In this lesson she uses long e, long a, long o. She tells students to

listen for long e and long a in column (1); then for long e and long o in column (2):

Column (1)		Column (2)	
ē	ā	ē	ō
we	way	see	so
eat	ate	tea	toe
meal	mail	these	those
please	plays	knee	know

5. Rhythms of grammatical forms and expressions. Students know the first three words and listen for the last word without seeing the teacher's lips. They repeat the last word:

Please pass the . . . . [bread]
Please pass the . . . . [potatoes]
Please pass the . . . . [salt]
Please pass the . . . . [butter]
Please pass the . . . . [sugar]
Please pass the . . . . [cream]

Discrimination of Word Details. Pupils are taught to discriminate between word details by a variety of means.

1. Left-out parts of sentences which are completed by the students:

Father said, "Did you wash your . . . ?" [hands]
Don't stand up in your . . . . [chair]
Table manners are how we act at . . . . [the table]
We must remember to be . . . . [polite]
Mother asked Tommy to say . . . . [a prayer]
Tommy wanted to be a . . . . [nice boy]

2. Sentences finished by students from fragments of words which the teacher gives. Many children with a severe hearing impairment hear only fragments of words and learn to complete them from the context.

Dō mā sō mŭ noi	Don't make so much noise.
Plē pă th brĕ	Please pass the bread.
Im hŭn	I'm hungry.

3. Breakdown of words into movements. This exercise is given last so that the students will not develop any overanalytical habits. This lesson is on long vowels and the diphthong oi. The students have now been exposed to the vocabulary of the dialogue without analyzing the movements of the words seen.

The movements: long vowels ē, ā, ī, ō, and ä (ah), diphthong oi. (A diphthong is the blending of two vowel sounds into one syllable, oi = aw-ē.) The teacher asks the following questions in order to get the six words on the blackboard: please, table, nice, Father, elbows, noise.

What should we say when we ask for something?	Please.
Where was Fred sitting?	At the table.
What kind of boy did Tommy want to be?	A nice boy.
Who went to help Mother in the kitchen?	Father.
What shouldn't we put on the table?	Elbows.
What was Fred doing that was not polite?	Making funny noises.

Students may select the rest of the vocabulary from the dialogue to illustrate the long vowels and the diphthong.

4. Homophenous words. Homophenous words are those that look alike on the lips but may sound differently, i.e.,

face	Tommy washed his hands and *face* before eating.
vase	There are pretty yellow flowers in the *vase*.
make	We must not *make* funny noises at the table.
bake	Do you know how to *bake* a cake?
bad	Tommy was not a *bad* boy.
pan	Mother put the *pan* of potatoes on the stove.
man	Father is a nice *man*.

manners   Tommy wanted to learn about good table *manners.*

matters   Important *matters* kept Father at the office until 7 o'clock.

Expansion of Vocabulary

The basic purpose of the use of life-situation films is, of course, to increase the children's fund of information, vocabulary, and insight into situations by introducing related exercises, topics, and games, and by using words in different contexts.

Dramatizations. Extensive use of dramatization may be made as children are encouraged to: (1) dramatize good and bad table manners and (2) develop good rules.

Be clean when you come to the table.

Sit quietly (don't stand in the chair, don't make noises, and don't play with things on the table).

Watch and listen when others are speaking.

Start to eat when all are seated at the table.

Don't reach for your food across the table.

Games. The following are illustrative of the games which may be devised:

1. Guessing game on food. Teacher gives a letter and students name a fruit or vegetable beginning with that letter:

A—apple, apricots   C—carrots, cauliflower

B—banana   P—potatoes

F—figs   T—tomatoes

2. "Where?" Students give the answers:

Where was Mother?	In the kitchen.
Where was the bread?	On the table.
Where was Tommy standing?	In his chair.
Where did Father go?	Into the kitchen.
Where did Father put the potatoes?	On the table.
Where did Tommy put his elbows?	On the table.

3. Contrast words. Students put words into sentences:

polite	rude
noise	quiet
clean	dirty
sit down	stand up
bad manners	good manners
nice	bad

Bibliography

Bennett, Daphne Nicholson. "Some Aspects of Motion Picture Technique in Language Rehabilitation," *Exceptional Children*, 25:113–19, (Nov. 11) 1958.

Bruhn, Martha E. *The Muller-Walle Method of Lip-Reading for the Deaf.* Thomas P. Nichols, Lynn, Mass., 1920.

Bunger, Anna M. *Speech Reading—Jena Method.* Interstate, Danville, Ill., 1944.

DeLand, Fred. *The Story of Lip Reading, Its Genesis and Development,* revised by Harriet Andrews Montague. Volta Bureau, Washington, D.C., 1931.

Ewing, Irene R. *Lip Reading and Hearing Aids.* Manchester University Press, Manchester, England, 1944.

Kinzie, Cora Elsie, and Rose Kinzie. *Lip Reading for the Deafened Adult.* John C. Winston Company, Philadelphia, 1931.

Lamoreaux, Lillian A., and Dorris May Lee. *Learning to Read Through Experience.* D. Appleton-Century Company, Inc., New York, 1943.

Morkovin, B. V., and Lucelia M. Moore. *Life Situation Speechreading Through the Cooperation of Senses.* A Manual, Bookstore, University of Southern California, Los Angeles 7, California, 1949.

Morkovin, Boris V., and Lucelia M. Moore. *A Guide to Life-Situation Films.* Cinema Department of the University of Southern California, Los Angeles, 1959.

Morkovin, Boris V., and Lucelia M. Moore. *Life-Situation Films,* Series II (in color and with sound). Cinema Department of the University of Southern California, Los Angeles, 1959.

Nitchie, Edward B. *Lip Reading, Principles and Practice.* Frederick A. Stokes Company, Philadelphia, 1919.

PART VIII

ON HIS FEET

SECTION 1

CHANGING ATTITUDES, CHANGING STANDARDS

Case histories of deaf persons who have "made good" show the importance of their urge for self-improvement as possibly the most important aspect of their habilitation.

An outstanding example of this is the experience of James Marsters, who was born deaf. Yet his profound deafness did not prevent him from attending public schools in New York City, from preparing himself for college, and from becoming a successful professional man. With the encouragement of family and friends who believed in him, he was able to break through the formidable barriers of deafness and isolation.

The decision to cast his lot with those who communicate orally rather than with those who prefer to use the manual alphabet and sign language made him realize soon that, in the world of competition, people do not make special allowances for any man's handicap, and that he himself must overcome his deafness. He simply had to "go an extra mile" in his own efforts and work in order to meet competition if he were ever to succeed as a professional man.

A few incidents during several crucial periods in Dr. James Marsters' life will serve to illustrate the importance of his viewpoint.

125

SECTION 2

"I CHOSE THE HEARING WORLD"
An Interview with
James C. Marsters[1]

"Yesterday's standards of a deaf person in the hearing world are no longer with us—we have gone forward." Dr. James Marsters bases this conviction on the long experience of his own profound deafness and on that of the deaf professional people he has known—doctors, lawyers, chemists, authors, businessmen, and others.

Dr. Marsters lost his hearing bilaterally from scarlet fever at the age of three months. Until the age of thirteen, when he began to use hearing aids, he never had the experience of hearing sounds, even though he did feel vibration.

"There are many erroneous opinions about the deaf," says Dr. Marsters. "I was told from my earliest childhood that I couldn't talk, but I do. I was told I couldn't drive, fly, go to college, become a doctor, but I have done all of these; I couldn't be drafted, but my papers say that I'm fully inductable as a practicing dentist."

Dr. Marsters feels strongly that a deaf child of average or better-than-average intelligence can become adjusted to the hearing world and can eventually occupy a position according to his abilities.

"Hundreds of voices chorus with me. . . . There is little or nothing your deaf child cannot do, given an encouraging hand, an opportunity of following his own interests, and a willingness to learn from his own mistakes. . . . Let's help him to use his abilities, which we often do not recognize, do not encourage, or simply smother. Let's help him to use his own hands, voice, and mind, and give him love that sets him free to grow and live."

[1] James C. Marsters, B.S., M.S., D.D.S., dental surgeon, instructor, and clinician, Dental College, University of Southern California, Department of Orthodontics.

Obstacles to Be Overcome

The development of the deaf child's potentialities is delayed by his handicap of deafness and isolation. But the wrong attitude and ignorance of those who are supposed to guide him doubly compound the difficulty.

Dr. Marsters believes that ". . . overprotection and pity are the worst offenses—i.e., thinking, speaking, and doing things for the deaf child which he can do himself. They rob him of self-confidence and endanger his future life by inducing him to look for easy ways out of situations without making any effort on his part."

Equally bad for the child is the opposite—rejection by his parents who resent his deafness and do not speak to him since "he would not understand anyway." In this environment, the child becomes dissociated from others and fails to comprehend what is going on around him.

Dr. Marsters adds: "I wish people could visualize what such an isolation means and does to the deaf child. Left alone in his silent world he becomes utterly confused, frustrated, and withdraws into his shell. In school he lacks self-confidence and initiative to fit into the class."

Participation

Fortunately for him, "Jimmy's" family had an understanding of his problem. They treated him as a normal child, and he was made to feel that he was a part of the family group. "They let me enjoy vicariously what others were hearing, enjoy the radio through their ears, laugh when they laughed, do things with them, and participate in the discussion of the family problems. They encouraged me to go ahead and to investigate uncertain provinces without drumming into me, 'No, no, no!' I had plenty of opportunities to follow my interests and to be stimulated in my speech, personality, and social development."

In this connection, Dr. Marsters was asked to recall exactly how, as a child, he had been stimulated to enter into the closed world of speech—how the meanings of spoken words had first been understood. In preschool, little Jimmy was made conscious of speech and of the importance of the world of sound around him. In the Speech Clinic at Syracuse University, Dr. Harry Heltman made him aware of speech vibrations while holding him on his lap and letting him touch his throat and cheeks and at the same time those of his own. Jimmy became conscious of the muscular movements in his mouth while speaking. He associated this feeling of movements with the movements of his lips and tongue as he saw them in the mirror.

In his constant desire to attract attention of others, Jimmy was quick in observing ways to win the approval of those important to him. He learned table manners and other amenities from his aunt, of whom he was very fond. In public school he learned to take turns with other children and to follow the rules of the game. He and his older brother learned some magic tricks when he received a Gilbert Magic set on his ninth birthday. At thirteen, he became popular both in and out of school and won many friends and admirers by his unusual dexterity and skill as a magician. In the Scout movement he found a source of new knowledge, skills, and recognition. He earned the title of an "Eagle Scout with Palms," at that time the highest award.

At the same time, Jimmy became seriously interested in science and in the use of science for human welfare. He wanted to serve human beings and to become a doctor.

"No Easy Way"

In his teens, Jim realized that in order to "become somebody" in the hearing world he would have to work harder than other people. At the age of fifteen, he entered the Wright Oral School for the Deaf, in New York City, to prepare himself for college. There he had to face the fact that he had "slovenly speech, pronunciation, and a nasal accent . . . ; probably I did it so that I could better feel vibrations in my nose." It was made clear to him that he could not expect any consideration for his deafness if he wanted to become a professional man. There was no other way but to study and to make a determined effort to learn from his mistakes. He joined a "merit system" group, which involved constant self-criticism and criticism by other students and teachers. He was watched and corrected mercilessly for his accent, intonation, and pronunciation. The strenuous work and exercises helped him to understand better and more accurately the difference between good and bad speech.

"I was not aware that I had been cutting consonants or pronouncing words and sentences without completing them until it was repeatedly brought to my attention. . . . I had a 'lazy' soft palate and flat tongue and I had to work on them diligently. I became aware that people use their voices melodiously, with accents and with rhythm. With the help of the teacher and by closer observation on my part I improved my voice. I read aloud from books to my teacher, and she corrected me until I developed a habit of speaking more accurately.

"In the case of mispronouncing words we had to look them up in the dictionary for pronunciation and meaning. The school was very strict, did not allow us to use sign language, and objected to our social contacts with 'signers' in order to prevent us from slipping back to the 'easy way' in our communication.

"The work of speech and language never ends. Even today, I find myself slipping at times and mispronouncing words, so I encourage my friends and even strangers not to hesitate to correct me. I do not feel embarrassed by my mistakes, and am thankful for their help. At times, I can laugh with my friends at some of my funny mistakes."

Dr. Marsters at the present time has a large orthodontist practice in Pasadena and performs corrective dental surgery. He teaches at the university, keeps abreast of developments in his profession, and maintains a wide range of scientific and general interests. He excels in fencing, boxing, swimming, and tennis. He is a public speaker and can enter readily into conversation with strangers on many subjects.

Bibliography

Gorman, Pierre. "A Study in the Integration of the Auditorially Handicapped into General Society." Unpublished thesis, College of Corpus Christi, Cambridge University, England, 1952.

Heckman, Helen. *My Life Transformed.* The Macmillan Company, New York, 1928.

Keller, Helen. *The Story of My Life.* Doubleday, Page & Company, New York, 1903.

Skorokhodova, Olga. *How I Perceive the World.* Academy of Pedagogical Sciences, Moscow, 1947.

Wright, H. F. "The Influence of Barriers upon Strength of Motivation," *Contributions to Psychology Theory.* Vol. I, No. 3, Duke University Press, Durham, North Carolina, 1937.

PART IX

CONCLUSION

DEVELOPMENT OF THE HEARING-IMPAIRED CHILD'S POTENTIALITIES

This book considers the hearing-impaired child's learning of speechreading, speech, and language from the point of view of the development of his effective oral communication. The techniques and materials presented here suggest ways of initiating and improving his oral communication. This communication must serve his needs and help him to adapt to an oral environment and to live up to the requirements of his teachers. In order to achieve this goal it is necessary to involve his whole personality—his sensory and mental capacities—in learning activities which challenge him.

The process of helping the child to achieve his potentialities is now being facilitated by the contributions of modern medicine and electronics. When the child is examined medically at an early age, it is often possible to preserve the maximum of his hearing and to alleviate much of his deafness. Scientific improvements in the fitting of hearing aids now make it possible even for the child with severe hearing impairment to profit greatly and to make maximum use of the remnants of hearing left to him.

It is essential that the child's parents and teachers understand the underlying psychological factors which promote or hinder his oral communication. Optimal conditions should be created to foster his orientation and a feeling of security in his environment. He should be helped in play and in many varied activities to size up simple situations and their purposes and to enter into reassuring and pleasant interpersonal relations. He should be surrounded by an oral atmosphere and encouraged to imitate speech in connection with the situations familiar to him. In his speechreading and speech he should acquire a working vocabulary to be used functionally in coping with his simple routine and play situations. The words which he acquires should gradually become a living instrument which actively influences his behavior and helps him to assert himself and participate in the happenings around him.

The Beginnings of Communication

Every normal child, hearing or deaf, is bursting with curiosity; he simply loves to explore and experiment. The hearing-impaired child is basically no different in his innate psychological endowment. His "dynamics" are also characterized by a search for discovery and desire to communicate with others. The time to capitalize upon his native endowment is at the time when these traits first appear. A successful beginning is highly important. If the child is deprived of a conducive atmosphere, he may easily be set back or be so frustrated that his first attempts to understand others and to express himself become almost his last efforts in that direction. The wrong atmosphere may create in him a block to learning and become so deadening that he loses all interest in using his voice for imitating speech. Making a game out of associating residual sounds and lip movements with words is an accomplishment which is worth any amount of special effort, study, patience, and enthusiasm on the part of parents and teachers.

When the child responds positively to the relaxed, congenial flow of communication, he becomes more and more alert to every sign, every sensory and circumstantial intimation which can tip him off to the meaning of the situation and the intent of the speaker. Like a detective, he begins to watch for every clue which will throw light or suggest meanings. Words are easily connected with actions, objects, expressions, posture, and gestures. It is a great victory to the child and to his parents and teachers when the child's cooperation is won. The experience marks the inception of the humanization of the child —his entrance into lasting and articulate human relationships, if only through the imitation of those he loves, for these are the ones who will become his models. The wheels of rudimentary oral communication begin to turn. His successful communication engenders alertness, both mental and physical, a trait which is of utmost importance if he is to break through the barriers of social isolation. As the game of communication engrosses the child's attention, it becomes a part of his basic pattern. Alertness engenders better powers of observation, an increased span of attention, and keener acuity. Stage by stage, the child grows in his ability to communicate orally. Under the insightful and patient handling by parents and teachers, he is gradually enabled to orient himself in the world of widening relationships and activities.

Adaptation to the Oral Environment

In the process of the child's adjustment to his environment, he is encouraged to use his sensory and mental capacities. If the atmosphere is a congenial one in which an understanding family speaks to him constantly, he soon becomes an active participant in everyday living and playing. With the use of a hearing aid at an early age, he experiences and responds to a multiplicity of environmental sounds. He learns, with the help of those about him, to recognize differences in sounds and to use them as landmarks in play situations and events in which he participates. His interaction with his environment is enhanced if his hearing aid helps him to hear some speech sounds and if he can associate these sounds with the moving lips of the speaker. In this way the auditory cues of speech are supplemented for him with the visual ones. His efforts at imitation and self-expression give great delight to his family. He learns to recognize the vibrations of speech by touching his own cheeks and throat and those of his mother and others. With the help of his mother or teacher he becomes aware of the kinesthetic movements by "feeling" them in his mouth while speaking and associating them with speech. The sensory coordination of hearing, sight, touch, and kinesthesis assists him in his progress toward oral communication in the context of meaningful situations. The surrounding world ceases to be a meaningless or frightening place as the child slowly becomes oriented to his world. He begins to understand the intentions and expectations of others and is able to express his needs. His speechreading becomes an intellectual skill[1] which grows as he orients himself and understands the relationships between people and the different functions of objects. His mind is gradually freed from the imprisonment of deafness and social isolation.

Development of Language

It is a long and laborious journey for the child with a serious hearing deficiency to reach the goal of mastering oral and written language. There are many sensory and mental dimensions to language. In learning the skills of effective oral communication, the child becomes a part of several different environments—home, school, community—each of which increases his powers of observation and association.

Many suggestions to meaning are opened to him, some verbal, but many nonverbal. At the outset, he connects words as he sees them, hears them, or "feels" them with firsthand nonverbal impressions in the immediate situation. In his school studies, he learns more about the verbal aspects of language. He learns the principles of language structure; he perceives that there are logical connections between words and ideas. A number of specialized audiovisual aids for speechreading, such as the life-situation films,[2] have been devised to help him as he develops verbal intellectual skills, and his attention is trained to analyze and synthesize verbal expressions with the help of visual details.

In language there are special difficulties for him—understanding the use of metaphors, distinguishing between words of several mean-

---

[1] "Speechreading is essentially an intellectual exercise; the mechanical part performed by the eye . . . is entirely subsidiary. The aim of the speechreader should be to grasp a speaker's meaning." From a speech by Mrs. Alexander Graham Bell at a Chautauqua meeting in 1894. See *The Story of Lip Reading, Its Genesis and Development* by Fred DeLand (revised by Harriet Andrews Montague), published by the Volta Bureau, Washington, D.C., 1931.

[2] Life-situation films, see Part VII.

ings, finding precise meanings for abstract concepts of causal or conditional relationships, and understanding the principles of grammatical and syntactic structure of language. Only through skilled and creative teaching can these abstractions be clarified, illustrated, and made concrete. These abstract concepts are developed by means of excursions, exhibits, visual aids, classroom discussions, and dramatizations. They are also vitalized through school projects which lead the child to do extensive reading, consulting encyclopedias, and hunting answers from a variety of sources.

The development of effective language is inextricably connected with the growth of experience, because experience underlies language, and language organizes experience. In order to expedite successful communication and to promote the growth of the child's personality, his language teaching must be supported by the enrichment of his experience and knowledge. His learning should be vitalized and reinforced by his active involvement in the various happenings of his oral environment.

In the child's play and living situations he learns to function as a member of a little community. This community serves at the same time as a sort of laboratory for the development of language. He does not acquire language mechanically. He uses it functionally in expressing his emotions and needs, in learning to understand and respond to others, and in sharing with them his interests, wants, and experiences. As the child's language, speech, and speechreading skills develop, he is stimulated to meet new situations and to solve new problems.

The Effect of an Oral Atmosphere and the Child's Effort toward Self-correction

The more opportunities a hearing-impaired child has for effective oral communication with hearing children, the more quickly he will acquire habits of oral communication and the greater his chance of improving his speech and speechreading. The question as to whether or not he will be able to join his hearing contemporaries in school depends upon the individual child. Whether he will be able to join them in the elementary school, or in the high school, or not till later in a school of higher learning can only be decided individually for each child. No generalization should be made. Each individual child should be examined and considered separately on the basis of his sensory and mental capacities; the effectiveness of his use of hearing aids; his proficiency in speech, speechreading, and language arts; and his general readiness. In most cases, he will need to be prepared by a specially trained teacher of the hard of hearing or deaf, or be prepared in a school for the deaf.

A child of average or above-average ability, even with a severe hearing impairment, can usually be integrated successfully with his oral environment if given opportunities to study and play with hearing children. One of the most important factors in his integration is his own effort, and his eventual ability to live up to the standards of effective oral communication. His conscious striving for self-improvement and self-correction assists the work of his parents and teachers. If he is endowed with patience and a sense of humor so that he is able to laugh at some of his own mistakes, the task is made easier for all. The importance to the child's growth of his own self-reliance has been demonstrated by longitudinal studies or life histories of successful cases. It has also been confirmed by the reports of parents and teachers who have worked effectively in helping hearing-impaired children to break through the wall of isolation into active participation in the hearing-speaking world.

PART X

APPENDIXES

PERIODICALS HELPFUL TO PARENTS AND TEACHERS OF HEARING-IMPAIRED CHILDREN

American Annals of the Deaf. Editorial office, Gallaudet College, Kendall Green, Washington 2, D.C. For educators of the deaf.

Hearing News. Editorial office, 919 18th St., N.W., Washington 6, D.C. The official publication of the American Hearing Society.

Journal of Exceptional Children. Editorial office, Michigan State Normal College, Ypsilanti, Michigan. The official publication of the International Council of Exceptional Children.

The Journal of Speech and Hearing Disorders. Editorial office, 321 Illini Hall, University of Illinois, Urbana, Illinois. The official publication of the American Speech and Hearing Association, devoted to the technical problems of speech and hearing.

Laryngoscope. Editorial office, 640 S. Kingshighway, St. Louis 10, Missouri. A technical medical journal of the American Laryngological, Rhinological and Otological Society, Inc.

The Volta Review. Editorial office, 1537 35th St., N.W., Washington 7, D.C. The official publication of the Volta Bureau, Alexander Graham Bell Association for the Deaf, Inc.

SPECIALIZED HEARING SERVICES

Alabama

Auburn   Speech and Hearing Clinic, Alabama Polyclinic Institute

Birmingham   Birmingham Speech and Hearing Center, 704½ S. 18th St.

Hearing and Speech Clinic, Medical College of Alabama, 1919 7th Ave. S.

Florence   Speech and Hearing Center, Florence State College

Montevallo   Alabama College Speech and Hearing Clinic

Tuscaloosa   Speech and Hearing Clinic, University of Alabama

Arkansas

Conway   Speech and Hearing Clinic, Arkansas State Teachers College

Fayetteville   Speech Clinic, University of Arkansas, 2nd Floor, Old Main

California

Chico   Speech and Hearing Clinic, Chico State College

Fresno   Fresno State College, Speech and Hearing Clinic

Los Angeles   Diagnostic Hearing Evaluation and Hearing Aid Selection Clinic, Los Angeles State College, 5151 Murphy St., 32

Speech and Hearing Clinic, University of California at Los Angeles, 24

	Speech and Hearing Clinic, University of Southern California, 930 W. 37th St., 7
San Francisco	Audiology and Speech Clinic, University of California Medical Center, 3rd and Parnassus Sts.
	Speech and Hearing Clinic, San Francisco State College
San Jose	Speech and Hearing Center, San Jose State College
Stanford	Stanford Speech and Hearing Clinic, Division of Speech Pathology and Audiology, Stanford University
Stockton	Speech and Hearing Clinic, College of the Pacific
Whittier	Speech and Hearing Clinic, Whittier College

Colorado

Boulder	Speech and Hearing Clinic, University of Colorado
Denver	Hearing Center, University of Denver, 10
Greeley	Speech and Hearing Clinic, Colorado State College

Connecticut

Storrs	Speech and Hearing Clinic, University of Connecticut
New Haven	Hearing and Speech Center, Yale-New Haven Medical Center, 789 Howard Ave.

Delaware

Wilmington	Audiology and Speech Center, Delaware Hospital, 501 W. 14th St.

District of Columbia

Washington	Speech and Hearing Clinic, Catholic University, 4th St. at Michigan Ave., N.W., 17

Florida

Coral Gables	Speech and Hearing Clinic, University of Miami
Gainsville	Speech and Hearing Clinic, University of Florida, 339 Administration Building
Tallahassee	Speech and Hearing Clinic, Florida State University

Georgia

Athens   Speech and Hearing Clinic, University of Georgia

Hawaii

Honolulu   Speech and Hearing Center, University of Hawaii

Illinois

Carbondale   Speech and Hearing Clinic, Southern Illinois University

Charleston   Speech and Hearing Clinic, Eastern Illinois University

Chicago   Hearing Clinic, Northwestern University, 303 E. Chicago Ave.

                        Speech and Hearing Center, Eye and Ear Infirmary, University of Illinois, 904 W. Adams St.

                        Speech and Hearing Clinic, University of Chicago, 950 E. 59th St., 37

DeKalb   Speech and Hearing Clinic, Northern Illinois University

Evanston   Hearing Clinic, Northwestern University

Normal   Hearing Laboratory, Illinois State Normal University

Rockford   Speech Clinic, Rockford College

Urbana   University Hearing Center, University of Illinois, 322 Illini Hall

Indiana

Bloomington   Speech and Hearing Clinic, Indiana University

Indianapolis   Audiology and Speech Clinic, Indiana University Medical Center, 1100 W. Michigan St., 7

Lafayette   Speech and Hearing Clinic, Purdue University

Muncie   Ball State Speech & Hearing Clinic

Terre Haute   Special Education Clinic, Indiana State Teachers College

Iowa

Cedar Falls   Speech and Hearing Clinic, Iowa State Teachers College

Grinnell	Grinnell College Speech Clinic, Grinnell College
Iowa City	Department of Otolaryngology, University Hospitals

Kansas

Kansas City	Hearing and Speech Department, University of Kansas Medical Center, 39th and Rainbow
Lawrence	Speech and Hearing Clinic, University of Kansas, 4 Bailey Hall

Kentucky

Lexington	Audiology Clinic, Department of Psychology, University of Kentucky, 620 S. Limestone St.

Louisiana

Hammond	Special Education Clinic, Southeastern Louisiana College
Lafayette	Speech and Hearing Clinic, Southwestern Louisiana Institute
New Orleans	Tulane Speech and Hearing Clinic, Tulane Medical School, 12
Ruston	Speech Clinic, Louisiana Polytechnic Institute

Maryland

Baltimore	Department of Otolaryngology, University of Maryland, 1
	Hearing & Speech Center, Johns Hopkins School of Medicine and Hospital, 601 North Broadway, 5

Massachusetts

Boston	Speech and Hearing Center, Boston University, 332 Bay State Road
	Speech and Hearing Clinic, Emerson College, 130 Beacon St.

Michigan

Ann Arbor	Hearing Division, Speech Clinic, University of Michigan, 1007 E. Huron St.
Detroit	Speech and Hearing Clinic, Wayne State University, 656 W. Warren, 2

Michigan (*cont.*)

East Lansing   Speech and Hearing Clinic, Michigan State University

Ypsilanti   Eastern Michigan College

Minnesota

Duluth   Speech and Hearing Clinic, University of Minnesota, Duluth Branch, 5

Minneapolis   Audiology Clinic, University of Minnesota Hospital

Speech and Hearing Clinic, University of Minnesota, 14

Mississippi

Hattiesburg   Speech and Hearing Clinic, Mississippi Southern College

Missouri

Cape Girardeau   Speech and Hearing Clinic, Southeast Missouri State College

Columbia   Speech and Hearing Clinic, University of Missouri, Parker Hall

St. Louis   Hearing Service, Central Institute for the Deaf, 818 S. Kingshighway, 10

Speech Clinic, St. Louis University, 3650 Lindell Blvd.

Washington University

Montana

Billings   Eastern Montana Speech and Hearing Clinic, Eastern Montana College of Education

Nebraska

Kearney   Speech Clinic, Nebraska State College

Lincoln   Speech and Hearing Laboratories, University of Nebraska, 102C Temple, 12th and R Sts.

New Mexico

Albuquerque   Speech and Hearing Clinic, University of New Mexico

New York

Brooklyn   Speech and Hearing Center, Brooklyn College, Bedford Ave. at Avenue H, 10

Garden City   Speech and Hearing Center, Adelphi College

New York   Hofheimer Speech and Hearing Clinic, Columbia Presbyterian Medical Center, 622 West 168th St., 32

Speech and Hearing Center, Hunter College, 695 Park Ave., 21

Speech and Hearing Center, New York Hospital–Cornell Medical Center, 525 E. 68th St., 21

Speech and Hearing Therapy Department, Institute of Physical Medicine, New York University–Bellevue Medical Center, 400 E. 34th St., 16

Syracuse   Dr. Gordon D. Hoople Hearing and Speech Center, Syracuse University, 805 S. Crouse Ave.

North Carolina

Durham   Speech and Hearing Center, Duke University Medical Center

Greenville   Speech and Hearing Clinic, East Carolina College

Winston-Salem   Hearing and Speech Center, Bowman Gray School of Medicine, North Carolina Baptist Hospital

North Dakota

Grand Forks   Speech and Hearing Clinic, University of North Dakota, 17 Merrifield Hall

Ohio

Athens   Children's Speech and Hearing Clinic, Ohio University

Bowling Green   Speech and Hearing Clinic, Bowling Green State University

Cleveland   Cleveland Hearing and Speech Center, Affiliated with Western Reserve University, 11206 Euclid Ave.

Columbus   Speech and Hearing Clinic, Ohio State University

Kent   Hearing Clinic, Kent State University

Ohio (*cont.*)

Oxford   Speech and Hearing Clinic, Miami University

Oklahoma

Oklahoma City   Speech and Hearing Clinic, University of Oklahoma

Tahlequah   Speech and Hearing Clinic, Northeastern State College

Tulsa   Speech and Hearing Clinic, Tulsa University

Oregon

Eugene   Speech and Hearing Clinic, University of Oregon

Pennsylvania

Bloomsburg   Speech and Hearing Clinic, State Teachers College

Indiana   Speech and Hearing Clinic, State Teachers College

Philadelphia   Audiology Section, Temple University Medical Center, 3401 N. Broad St., 40

                          Hearing and Speech Center, Jefferson Medical College Hospital, 1015 Walnut St., 7

                          Speech and Hearing Center, Hospital of the University of Pennsylvania, 36th and Spruce Sts., 4

                          Speech and Hearing Center, Temple University, 22

University Park   Speech and Hearing Clinic, Pennsylvania State University

South Carolina

Charleston   Speech and Hearing Center, Medical College of South Carolina, 55 Doughty St.

South Dakota

Vermillion   Speech and Hearing Clinic, University of South Dakota

Tennessee

Johnson City   Speech and Hearing Center, East Tennessee State College

Knoxville   East Tennessee Hearing and Speech Center, University of Tennessee Campus

Memphis	Memphis Speech and Hearing Center, University of Tennessee, 874 Monroe

Texas

Austin	Speech and Hearing Clinic, University of Texas
Dallas	Speech and Hearing Clinic, Southern Methodist University
Denton	Speech and Hearing Clinic, State College for Women
Fort Worth	Speech, Hearing and Retardation Clinic, Texas Christian University
Galveston	Hearing and Speech Clinic, University of Texas Medical Branch
Houston	Speech and Hearing Clinic, University of Houston, 3801 Cullen Blvd.
San Antonio	Speech and Hearing Clinic, Our Lady of the Lake College
San Marcos	Southwest Texas State Teachers College
Waco	Speech and Hearing Clinic, Baylor University

Utah

Provo	Speech and Hearing Clinic, Brigham Young University
Salt Lake City	Speech and Hearing Center, University of Utah, 1699 E. 5th, S.

Virginia

Charlottesville	Speech and Hearing Center, University of Virginia
Richmond	Hearing and Speech Center, Medical College of Virginia, Box 846, 231 N. 12th St.

Washington

Seattle	Speech and Hearing Clinic, University of Washington, 1320 Campus Parkway

West Virginia

Morgantown	Speech and Hearing Clinic, West Virginia University

Wisconsin

Madison   Speech and Hearing Clinic, University of Wisconsin,
                       403 Bascom Hall

Milwaukee   Hearing Evaluation Center, University of Wisconsin,
                       3203 N. Downer Ave.

                       Hearing Laboratory, School of Speech, Marquette
                       University, 625 N. 15th St., 3

Wyoming

Laramie   Wyoming Speech and Hearing Clinic, University of
                       Wyoming

APPENDIX 3

PUBLIC RESIDENTIAL SCHOOLS FOR THE DEAF
IN THE UNITED STATES

Alabama

Talladega — Alabama School for the Deaf, 205 E. South St.

Alabama School for Negro Deaf, P.O. Box 457

Arizona

Tucson — Arizona State School for the Deaf and Blind

Arkansas

Little Rock — Arkansas School for the Deaf, 2400 Markham St.

Arkansas School for Negro Deaf, 4701 W. 20th St.

California

Berkeley — California School for the Deaf, 2601 Warring St.

Riverside — California School for the Deaf, P.O. Box 2081

Colorado

Colorado Springs — Colorado School for the Deaf and Blind

Connecticut

West Hartford — American School for the Deaf, 139 N. Main St.

Mystic — Mystic Oral School for the Deaf

District of Columbia

Washington — Gallaudet College, Kendall Green, 2
Kendall School for the Deaf, Kendall Green, 2

Florida

St. Augustine   Florida School for the Deaf and Blind, San Marco Ave.
School for the Negro Deaf, San Marco Ave.

Georgia

Cave Springs   Georgia School for the Deaf

Hawaii

Honolulu   Hawaii Diamond Head School, 3440 Leahi Ave., 15

Idaho

Gooding   Idaho State School for Deaf and Blind, 14th Ave. and
Main

Illinois

Jacksonville   Illinois School for the Deaf, 125 S. Webster

Indiana

Indianapolis   Indiana State School for the Deaf, 1200 E. 42nd St., 5

Iowa

Council Bluffs   Iowa School for the Deaf

Kansas

Olathe   Kansas School for the Deaf

Kentucky

Danville   Kentucky School for the Deaf

Louisiana

Baton Rouge   State School for the Deaf, 800 St. Ferdinand St., 1
State School for Deaf Negroes, Scotlandville, 7

Maine

Portland   Governor Baxter State School for Deaf, P.O. Box 799

Maryland

Frederick   Maryland School for the Deaf, South Market St.

Massachusetts

Beverly	Beverly School for the Deaf, 6 Echo Ave.
Northampton	Clarke School for the Deaf, Round Hill Rd.
Randolph	Boston School for the Deaf, 800 N. Main St.

Michigan

Flint	Michigan School for the Deaf, W. Court St., 4

Minnesota

Faribault	Minnesota School for the Deaf, Box 440

Mississippi

Jackson	Mississippi School for the Deaf, Box 4483 Fondren Sta.
	School for the Negro Deaf, Green St.

Missouri

Fulton	Missouri School for the Deaf, 5th & Vine

Montana

Great Falls	Montana School for the Deaf, 3800 2nd Ave., N

Nebraska

Omaha	Nebraska School for the Deaf, 3223 N. 45th St., 3

New Jersey

West Trenton	New Jersey School for the Deaf

New Mexico

Santa Fe	New Mexico School for the Deaf, 1060 Cerrillos Rd.

New York

Buffalo	St. Mary's School for the Deaf, 2253 Main St., 14
New York	Lexington School for the Deaf, 904 Lexington Ave., 21
	St. Joseph's School for the Deaf, 1000 Hutchinson River Parkway, 65
Rochester	Rochester School for the Deaf, 1545 St. Paul St., 21
Rome	Central New York School for the Deaf, 713 N. Madison St., 1
White Plains	New York School for the Deaf, 555 Knollwood Rd.

North Carolina

Morganton   School for the Deaf

Raleigh   State School for Blind and Deaf, Negro, 3320 Garner
                     Rd.

North Dakota

Devils Lake   North Dakota School for the Deaf

Ohio

Columbus   Ohio School for the Deaf, 500 Morse Rd., 14

Oklahoma

Sulphur   School for the Deaf, E. 10th & Tahlequah

Taft   The Consolidated Negro Institution

Oregon

Salem   Oregon State School for the Deaf, 999 Locust St.

Pennsylvania

Philadelphia   Pennsylvania School for the Deaf, Mt. Airy, 19

Pittsburgh   Western Pennsylvania School for Deaf, Edgewood, 18

Scranton   Pennsylvania State Oral School, 1800 N. Washington
                     Ave., 9

Rhode Island

Providence   Rhode Island School for the Deaf, 520 Hope St., 6

South Carolina

Spartanburg   School for Negro Deaf

                     South Carolina School for Deaf and Blind

South Dakota

Sioux Falls   South Dakota School for the Deaf, 1801 E. 10th St.

Tennessee

Knoxville   Tennessee School for the Deaf, Island Home Blvd., 20

Texas

Austin   Texas Blind, Deaf and Orphan School, 4205 Bull
                     Creek Rd.

                     Texas School for the Deaf, 1102 S. Congress, 4

Utah

Ogden   Utah Schools for the Deaf and Blind, 846 20th St.

Vermont

Brattleboro   Austine School, 120 Maple St.

Virginia

Hampton   Virginia State School

Staunton   School for the Deaf and Blind, Beverly St.

Washington

Vancouver   Washington State School for the Deaf, 611 Grand
                  Blvd.

West Virginia

Institute   School for the Colored Deaf and Blind

Romney   Schools for the Deaf and Blind

Wisconsin

Delevan   Wisconsin School for the Deaf, 309 W. Walworth Ave.

Wyoming

Casper   Wyoming School for the Deaf, 312 W. Midwest

PUBLIC DAY CLASSES
IN THE UNITED STATES

Alabama

Montgomery   100 Goode St.

California

Alhambra   100 S. Granada

Burlingame   High School, Carolan and Oak Grove Ave.
Roosevelt School, 1151 Vancouver Ave.

Carmichael   Starr King School, 1912 Mission Ave.

Ceres   Whitmore School, Box 307

Compton   Theodore Roosevelt School, 1927 E. San Vincente St.

Costa Mesa   Bay View Class, Box 517

Covina   Elementary School, 4070 Barranca St.

Fresno   Birney Oral Day Class, 2348 Mariposa St., 3

Garden Grove   Stanford School, 12721 Magnolia Ave.

Glendale   730 Glenwood

Hermosa Beach   Hermosa View School

La Mesa   6925 Tower St.

Lawndale   Centinela Valley, 4110—154th St.

Long Beach   Franklin Jr. High, 540 Cerritos Ave., 12
John Burroughs School, 1260 E. 33rd St., 7
Stevenson School, 515 Lime Ave., 12

Los Angeles   Hyde Park Blvd. School, 3140 Hyde Park Blvd., 43
Mary E. Bennet School, 166 S. Burlington Ave., 57
Secondary Classes, 1822 E. 7th St., 21

Norwalk	Norwalk School, 12820 Pioneer Blvd.
Oakland	Hamilton Jr. High School, 2101 35th Ave., 1
Orange	Sycamore School, 340 North Maine
Pasadena	McKinley Elementary School, 330 S. Oak Knoll Ave., 5
	McKinley Jr. High School, 325 S. Oak Knoll Ave., 5
Richmond	Nystrom School
Sacramento	Arden Carmichael Day Class School, 1912 Mission Ave., 21
San Diego	Mark Twain School, 4100 Normal St., 3
San Francisco	Gough Oral School, Washington & Gough Sts.
San Jose	Hester School, 408 Almaden
San Rafael	1055 Los Ovejas
Santa Monica	Madison School, 10th and Arizona
Santa Rosa	Steele Lane School, 301 Steele Lane
Stockton	1140 S. Pilgrim, 5
Tulare	Emergency School, 6110 Garden Ave.
Watsonville	Tri-County School, Martinelli St.

Colorado

Denver	Eiber School, 1401 Independence Ave., 15
	Evans School, 11th & Acoma, 4

Delaware

Wilmington	C. B. Lose School, 4th & Woodlawn Ave.

Florida

Miami	Miami Oral Classes, 275 N.W. 2nd St.
Orlando	Forest Park School, 1600 Silver Star

Illinois

Champaign	Franklin Jr. High, 817 N. Harris
	Oral Deaf School, 403 E. Healey St.
Chicago	Alexander Graham Bell Day School
	Carl Schurz High School, 3601 N. Milwaukee Ave.

Illinois,
Chicago (*cont.*)

	Chicago Vocational School for the Deaf—Oral Department
	Corkery School Class for Deaf
	Harrison High School, 2850 W. 24th
	Lake View High School
	Lane Technical High School
	Lowell School, Class for the Deaf
	Morrill School, 6110 S. Rockwell St.
	Parker High School, 6800 S. Stewart Ave.
Decatur	Washington School, 400 S. Maffit St.
East St. Louis	240 N. 6th St.
Elgin	Franklin School, Geneva St.
Elmhurst	Hawthorn School, 145 Arthur St.
Evanston	Colfax & McDaniel Sts.
Moline	1015 16th Ave.
Park Forest	Blackhawk School, 130 Blackhawk Dr.
Pekin	Franklin School, 100 Broadway
Peoria	Blaine Summer School, 919 S. Mathew
Quincy	1200 Maine St.
Springfield	Hay-Edwards School, 400–408 Lawrence
Waukegan	Central School, 128 N. County St.
Winnetka	Day School, 520 Glendale
Indiana	
Evansville	Glenwood Elementary Class, 901 Sweetser St., 13
Fort Wayne	Class for Deaf Nursery, Clinton & Pontiac Sts.
Gary	Oral Training Center, 600 E. 35th Ave.
Indianapolis	Speech & Hearing Center, 615 N. Alabama St., 4
Muncie	Harry Mock School
South Bend	Oral Day Class, 737 W. Beale St.
Iowa	
Davenport	1144 Main St.
Des Moines	Smouse Opportunity School, 28th and Center Sts., 12
Sioux City	2700 Leech St.

Kentucky

Covington   Center for Acoustically Handicapped, 1528 Scott St.

Louisville   Preschool Deaf Class, 1320 4th St.

Louisiana

New Orleans   4217 Orleans Ave.

Shreveport   Hamilton Terrace Jr. H.S., Louisiana St.
                 Line Ave. School, 1830 Line Ave.

West Shreveport Colored School, 2100 Weinstock St.

Maryland

Baltimore   Warwick & Windsor Aves., 16

Massachusetts

Boston   Health Department, 25 Blossom St.

Fitchburg   Fitchburg Habilitation Center, Outpatient Dept.,
                 Burbank Hospital

Lowell   Habilitation Center, 220 Worthen St.

Pittsfield   Habilitation Center, 193 Wendell Ave.
                 Mercer School, Orchard St.

Quincy   Habilitation Center, 1120 Hancock St.

Roxbury   Horace Mann School, Kearsarge Ave., 19

Salem   Habilitation Center, 5 Broad St.

South Dartmouth Habilitation Center, Sol-e-Mar Hospital

Springfield   Elias Brookings School, 367 Hancock St., 5

Waltham   Whittemore School, Parmenter Rd.

Watertown   Hosmer School, Winthrop St.

Worcester   Upsala Street School

Michigan

Battle Creek   Ann J. Kellogg School, Champion St.

Dearborn   Harvey H. Lowrey School, 6601 Jonathan

Detroit   6045 Stanton Ave., 8
                 Stephens School, 6006 Seneca, 13

Michigan (*cont.*)

Escanba	John A. Lemmer Elementary School
Ferndale	Coolidge School, 2521 Bermuda
Grand Rapids	1250 Sigsbee St. S.E., 6
Hamtramek	Day Class for Deaf, 9625 Lumpkin
Jackson	Allen St.
Kalamazoo	23 South Park, 35
Lansing	419 N. Cap
Muskegon	Marquette School, 480 Bennett St.
	Nelson School, Washington at 8th
Pontiac	Whitefield School, 2000 Orchard Lake
Royal Oak	Jefferson Elementary and Junior High, 2520 Nakota
Saginaw	3123 Court St.
Ypsilanti	Horace H. Rackham School, Rackham Dr.

Minnesota

Duluth	Public School, 2427 W. 4th St.
Minneapolis	Agassiz School, 3740 Harriet Ave., 8
	John Marshall High School, 14th Ave. & 5th St. S.E., 14
	Whittier School, 2609 Blaisdell
St. Paul	Central High School, Lexington & Marshall, 4
	Douglas Class, 90 Western Ave., 7
Winona	Lincoln School

Mississippi

Jackson	Magnolia Speech School

Missouri

Kansas City	Central Jr. High School
	Central Sr. High School
	Troost School, 5915 Forrest
	Wheatley School, 2415 Agnes St.
St. Louis	Gallaudet Day School, 1616 S. Grand Blvd., 4

New Jersey

Jersey City	182 Merseles St.

Newark	45 Bruce St., 3
Paterson	Public School No. 2, Passaic near Mill, 1
Woolbridge	Ross St.

New York

New York City — *Borough of Brooklyn:*
Eli Whitney High School, 257 N. 6th St., 11
Borough of Manhattan:
Bellevue Preschool Clinic, 26th St. & 1st Ave.
Charles Evans Hughes High School, 351 W. 18th St.
Hunter College Preschool Clinic, 695 Park Ave.
Junior High School 47, 225 E. 23rd St.
Mabel Dean Bacon Vocational High School, 129 E. 22nd St.
New York School of Printing, 439 W. 49th St.
Washington Irving Evening High School, 40 Irving Place
Borough of Queens:
William Cullen Bryant High School, 48-10 31st Ave., Long Island City, 3
Borough of Richmond:
Richmond Public School 40, 90 Henderson Ave., Richmond, Staten Island

Syracuse — Percy M. Hughes School, 345 Jamesville Ave., 10

Ohio

Akron — 366 Beaver St., 6

Canton — Belden Grade School, 2115 Georgetown Rd. N.E.
McKinley High School, 800 Market Ave. N., 2

Cincinnati — Cutter Junior High School, Broadway St.
Guilford, 421 East 4th St.
Hughes High School, 2515 Clifton Ave.
Hyde Park School, 3401 Edwards Rd.
Oakley School, 3086 Madison Road
Pleasant Ridge, 5945 Montgomery Road
Withrow Junior High School, Madison St.

Cleveland — Alexander Graham Bell School, 2390 E. 55th St., 4
Corlett School, 13013 Corlett Ave., 5

Ohio,
Cleveland (*cont.*)

	Stanard School, 5360 Stanard Ave., 3
	Willard School, 2220 W. 93, 2
Columbus	Indianola Elementary School, 140 16th Ave., 1
Dayton	Kennedy School, 240 Wyoming St., 6
East Cleveland	Chambers Elementary School, 14121 Shaw Ave.
	Mayfair Elementary School, 13916 Mayfair
Elyria	Hamilton School, Middle & 13th St.
Fremont	Atkinson School, Delaware Ave.
Kent	University School and DePeyster Elementary School
Lorain	W. 30th St.
Mansfield	75 Carpenter Road
Portsmouth	411 Court St.
Steubenville	Roosevelt School, Maryland Ave.
Toledo	Hamilton Elementary School, Manhattan Blvd., 6
	Jones Junior High School, Broadway & Walbridge Ave.
Youngstown	Adams Elementary School
Zanesville	Brighton Blvd.
	Sunshine School

Oklahoma

Tulsa	Central High School, 312 E. 6th, 3
	Horace Mann Jr. High School, 11th & Boston
	Longfellow School, 1240 E. 5th Place, 6

Oregon

Medford	Junior Service League Kdg., 606 Victory St.
Portland	Hosford School, 2303 S.E. 28th Place, 15

Pennsylvania

Erie	Wayne School, 6th & East Ave.
Philadelphia	Willis & Elizabeth Martin Public School, 22nd & Brown Sts., 30

Rhode Island

Providence	Windmill Street School, 110 Paul St.

Tennessee

Memphis   Idlewild School, 1950 Linden

Texas

Austin   Independent School, 701 E. 11th St.

Beaumont   1800 Pope

Corpus Christi   Corpus Christi School, Box 110

Dallas   Society for Crippled Children, 2312 Oak Lawn, 19

Edinburg   Roosevelt School for Exceptional Children

El Paso   Day Class

Fort Worth   958 Page, 4

Houston   1300 Capitol

Odessa   37th & McKnight

San Angelo   Special Ed. O.D., 224 N. Magdalen

Utah

Salt Lake City   University of Utah

Virginia

Norfolk   Meadow Brook School, Little Cr. Rd. & Shirland, 8

Washington

Seattle   Department of Deaf and Hard of Hearing, 815 4th Ave., 9

Spokane   Edna E. Davis School, 1723 W. 7th Ave., 43

Tacoma   East 50th and Roosevelt, 5

Yakima   Hoover School

West Virginia

Huntington   1341 5th Ave., 1

Wisconsin

Eau Claire   304 N. Dewey St.

Green Bay   525 S. Madison St.

Kenosha   6811 18th Ave.

Wisconsin (*cont.*)

La Crosse	Washburn School, 8th & Main Sts.
Madison	Lapham School, 1045 E. Dayton St.
Milwaukee	Lincoln Junior and Senior High, 820 E. Knapp St.
	Nee-ska-ra-Binner School, 1601 N. Hawley Rd., 8
Oshkosh	1109 Melvin Ave.
Racine	2326 Mohr Ave.
Shorewood	2100 E. Capitol Dr., 11
Stevens Point	Jackson Bldg., W. Clark St.
Superior	1812 Wyoming Ave.
Wausau	500 Randolph St.

MEMBER AGENCIES OF THE
AMERICAN HEARING SOCIETY

California

Los Angeles   Hearing Center of Metropolitan Los Angeles, 215 W. 5th St., 13

San Diego   San Diego Hearing Society, 3843 Herbert St., 3

San Francisco   San Francisco Hearing Society, Inc., 2015 Steiner St., 15

Colorado

Denver   Denver Hearing Society, Inc., 1556 Emerson St., 18

Connecticut

Hartford   Hartford Hearing League, Inc., 252 Asylum St., 3

District of Columbia

Washington   Washington Hearing Society, 1934 Calvert St., N.W., 9

Florida

Miami   Miami Hearing Society, 395 N.W. First St., 56

Georgia

Augusta   Augusta Speech and Hearing Center, 1030 Chafee Ave.

Illinois

Chicago   Chicago Hearing Society, 30 W. Washington St., Room 615, 2

Indiana

Indianapolis Indianapolis Speech and Hearing Center, 615 N. Alabama St., 4

South Bend Hearing and Speech Center of St. Joseph County, 511 W. Colfax Ave., 1

Iowa

Des Moines Des Moines Hearing and Speech Center, 615 Locust St., 9

Louisiana

New Orleans New Orleans League for Better Hearing, 165 Elk Place, 13

Maine

Portland Portland Hearing and Speech Center, Inc., 723-A Congress St., 3

Maryland

Baltimore Baltimore Hearing Society, Inc., 928 N. Charles St., 1

Massachusetts

Boston Boston Guild for the Hard of Hearing, 283 Commonwealth Ave., 15

Springfield Springfield Hearing League, 1694 Main St., 3

Worcester Worcester County Hearing and Speech Center, Inc., 214 Day Bldg., 306 Main St., 8

Michigan

Kalamazoo Constance Brown Society for Better Hearing, 316 Commerce Bldg., 111 N. Rose St.

Lansing Lansing Society for Better Hearing, 482 Hollister Bldg., 8

Michigan Association for Better Hearing, 408 Hollister Bldg., 8

Minnesota

Minneapolis Minneapolis Hearing Society, 1722 Hennepin Ave., 3

St. Paul St. Paul Hearing Society, 496 Endicott-on-Robert Bldg., 1

Missouri

St. Louis   St. Louis League for the Hard of Hearing, 4527 West-
minster Place, 8

New Jersey

Paterson   North Jersey Hearing and Speech Center, 7 Church
St.

New Mexico

Albuquerque   New Mexico Hearing Society, 1001 Second St., N.W.

New York

Mineola   Long Island Hearing and Speech Society, First St.

New York City   New York League for the Hard of Hearing, Inc., 480
Lexington Ave., 17

Rochester   Hearing and Speech Center of Rochester, Inc., 501
W. Main St., 8

Ohio

Cincinnati   Cincinnati Speech and Hearing Center, 3006 Vernon
Place, 19

Cleveland   Cleveland Hearing and Speech Center, Inc., 11206
Euclid Ave., 6

Columbus   Hearing and Speech Center of Columbus and Central
Ohio, 209 S. High St., 15

Dayton   Hearing and Speech Center of Dayton and Montgomery County, 1400 E. Third St., 3

Toledo   Toledo Hearing League, 2313 Ashland Ave., 10

Youngstown   Youngstown Hearing and Speech Center, 69 Illinois
Ave., 4

Oregon

Portland   Portland Center for Hearing and Speech, Inc., 2111
N.E. Weidler St., 12

Pennsylvania

Pittsburgh   Pittsburgh Hearing Society, Granite Bldg., 313 6th
Ave., 22

Rhode Island

Providence   Providence League for the Hard of Hearing, 42 Wey-
                      bosset St., 3

South Carolina

Columbia   Columbia Hearing Society, Forsythe Bldg., 915 Main
                      St.

Tennessee

Nashville   Nashville League for the Hard of Hearing, 120 21st
                      Ave., S., 4

Texas

Dallas   Dallas Hearing Society, 4222 Lemmon Ave., 4

Houston   Houston Speech and Hearing Center, 6504 Bertner
                      Ave.

Washington

Seattle   Seattle Hearing and Speech Center, Inc., 1229 10th
                      Ave., N., 2

Wisconsin

Madison   Hear Incorporated, 211 North Carroll St.

Milwaukee   Milwaukee Hearing Society, 757 N. Water St., 2

INDEX

Acceptance, of child. *See* Psychological aspects
Active life. *See* Functional method
Activities, involvement in. *See* Functional method
Alhambra Public Schools, Alhambra, California, 87, 98
American Annals of the Deaf, 141
American Genetics Association, 13
American Hearing Society, 165–68
Anticipation of words. *See* Speechreading
Approval, winning of. *See* Psychological aspects
Association. *See* Psychological aspects with lip movement. *See* Speechreading
Associative learning. *See* Learning
Attitudes. *See* Psychological aspects
Audiological aspects, 21–26
   audiograms, 59–60
   audiological considerations, 11
   audiologist, 24, 26
   audiometer, 18
     cycles per second (cps), 4, 21, 26
     response to, 21
   diagnosis, of deafness, 22–23
   ear mold, 23
   electronic devices, 18, 19
   evaluation of hearing, 17, 18, 21
   speech range, 4
   tests, audiometric, 17
Audiovisual aids, 72–94, 136
   animal lotto, 84
   animals, farm, 83
   bibliography, selected, 78, 82, 85, 86
   color, learning of, 40, 73–83

   mobile, 75
   wheel, 77
   concrete images, 72
   creative, role of teacher, 72
   flannel board, 34, 77
   games to play, 79–82
   gift making, 40
   job chart, 40, 41
   language. *See* Life-situation films, exercises
   materials, finding, 73–74
   presentation of, 74, 86
   motion pictures, educational, 57
     Life situation, 109–25
   objectives of, 74
   picture books, 34, 51
   picture painting, 58
   pictures, 35, 83
   puppets, 86
   sources of, 84
   speech, 81. *See also* Life-situation films, scripts of
   speechreading, 76, 81. *See also* Life-situation films
   television, 34, 57
Auditory training, 20, 21, 22–25, 58–61, 118
   amplification, 23, 60
   association, 23
   background noises, awareness of, 21–24
   demonstration of, 59–61
   discrimination of sound, 22, 23
   feedback, auditory, viii
   gross sounds, identification of, 60
   materials and procedures in, 60
   microphones, 23

JL